Praise for *I've*
Peer Support

MW00654995

As leaders in public safety departments, we all have a responsibility to do the right things for those we serve. Peer support teams ensure we're doing right by our own. *I've Got Your 6: Peer Support for First Responders* provides a clear outline for starting a team or improving the one you have.

Captain Dan Cohen,
Williamson County EMS Peer Support

First responders are a unique, often misunderstood group of individuals. Thank you for dedicating your career to our field so that you could provide our peer support team with the necessary tools to reenergize, revitalize, and rejuvenate our colleagues to find resiliency to live their best lives possible. I am proud to say those colleagues are my friends.

Shari Evans, RN,
Air Evac LifeTeam Peer Support
and Training Center Coordinator

This book is a must-have for any department/agency looking to establish a peer support program! Having been a part of the process of developing our program from the ground up and engaging with Tania early on, we followed the steps as outlined in this book and have transformed some of those "nay-sayers" into true believers. One of the keys to the overall success of our program has also been having Tania speak about the importance of peer support to our new recruits at the academy. When I saw the agents lined up to speak to Tania at the end of her segment, it brought me the greatest satisfaction, knowing she is breaking down the stigma of "sucking it up" and instead promoting good mental health from the onset of their careers.

Valerie McCarthy,
Federal Law Enforcement Agent (Retired),
Peer Support Team Leader

I'VE GOT YOUR 6

PEER SUPPORT FOR FIRST RESPONDERS

BY
TANIA GLENN, PSYD, LCSW, CCTP

RISING PHOENIX PRESS ®

Text Copyright © 2021 Tania Glenn
All rights reserved.

Published 2021 by
Progressive Rising Phoenix Press, LLC
www.progressiverisingphoenix.com

ISBN: 978-1-950560-47-9

Printed in the U.S.A.

Editor: Jody Amato

Author Photographs (Back Cover & Interior): "Tania Glenn" by Jill Hays, (www.jillhaysphotography.com). Used by permission of the photographer. © Copyright 2020 Jill Hays.

Colored Bull's-Eye
©2007 Jim Belk. Used by permission
https://en.wikipedia.org/wiki/File:Colored_Bullseye.png.

Diagram of Maslow's Hierarchy of Needs
© 2006 J. Finkelstein. Used by permission
https://commons.wikimedia.org/wiki/Commons:GNU_Free_D
ocumentation_License,_version_1.2.

Book cover and interior design by William Speir
Visit: http://www.williamspeir.com

Tania Glenn and Arya

Also by Tania Glenn:

First Responder Resilience: Caring for Public Servants

Code Four: Surviving and Thriving in Public Safety

First Responder Families: Caring for the Hidden Heroes

Smashing The Stigma and Changing the Culture in Emergency Services

Protected But Scared
(a book for the children of police officers)

This Is Our Normal
(a book for the children of first responders)

To peer support teams—
Thank you for being battle buddies.
Thank you for saving lives.

Table of Contents

Foreword

Mental health in the fire service is something that fire departments around the country are finally starting to address. The use of peer support and peer support teams is something that I feel is invaluable. Too many of our brothers and sisters have felt that there was no way out, and the only option was to end their lives. This is where peer support possibly could have saved them. The ability to have someone to talk to that you can truly relate to and understands what you are dealing with could make a huge difference in the decision that a person in crisis might make. Peer support can guide a person to finding the help that is right for them.

The hard part in establishing a peer support program is explaining why you need a team to leadership and getting the buy-in from the members of the department. So many times, I have talked to different teams and everyone has the same problem—they have a hard time figuring out where to start. This book is a blueprint on how to build a team—where to start and how to keep it going. Everyone seems to keep reinventing the wheel, but this book takes it back to the basics. Once you read this book, you will definitely understand what I am talking about.

Brandon Porter
Firefighter/Paramedic
Richardson Fire Department Peer Support

Introduction

What it means for me to be part of a team that is able to meet a coworker right where they are, in a place of darkness, is fulfilling.

Chris
REACH Air Medical Peer Support Team

The year 2020 has presented a multitude of challenges for first responders. Stress and trauma are at all-time high levels with little relief in sight. Earlier this year, I wrote the book, *Smashing the Stigma and Changing the Culture in Emergency Services,* to essentially hand over the keys to every agency to start the engine in creating change. Change has to occur to both eliminate the stigma and change the culture in public safety, thereby allowing first responders to get the help they need. No one is immune to stress, and public safety professionals are not robots. These professionals have hearts, minds, and they all have limits.

I consider *I've Got Your 6: Peer Support for First Responders* a follow-up book to *Smashing the Stigma and Changing the Culture in Emergency Services.* This book is written to help the agencies that have taken the keys and started their engines to now put their change process in motion and start moving forward.

I am in my twenty-ninth year of service to others. I have cared for the hearts and minds of first responders my entire career. I have been to everything from large-scale national disasters to small, local events and everything in between. I have traveled constantly, worked with multitudes of peer support teams, and have figured out what I consider to be best practices. I share my take on peer support not to say this is the only way to implement it, but to provide ideas, insight, and understanding on what it takes to run a successful peer support program, and to give readers ideas and resources to launch their own teams to fit their specific needs.

Everything I share here comes from wisdom, which I always say is hard-earned and causes gray hair. Much of my wisdom comes from difficult lessons and even mistakes. I share all of it because I want to contribute what I can to save the lives of first responders, who save the lives of so many more.

Chapter One

Reasons

My favorite thing about peer support is how much it has changed my department. It has taken away the belief that PTSD is something we just have to live with. It has normalized our struggles in a way that has made talking about them easier. It has taught us better ways to help each other when we recognize something isn't right. It's made it understandable to admit we're not ok and to take the time and the steps needed to recover. It has made us closer.

Doady
Fayette County EMS Peer Support Team

The concept of peer support has emerged out of need. Any study on first responders' rates of suicide, divorce, alcoholism, post-traumatic stress disorder, and other mental health problems will show that public safety professionals are at much higher rates and risks than the general population. While our first responders are trained and generally are desensitized to much of what they deal with, as they are exposed to increasing amounts of trauma and human suffering over time, every first responder has their limit. The limits are a threshold beyond which they are overwhelmed. Every first responder has a threshold for stress, and while the threshold expands over time and with good experience, there is a limit. First responders are not made of steel; they have hearts and minds like everyone else.

The types of events that are typically beyond the coping threshold of first responders include pediatric calls, events involving serious injury or death to other first responders, mass casualty incidents, significant carnage, known victims, or prolonged events ending with a negative outcome. When these occur, they typically push first responders well beyond their comfort zone of coping, and if they do not have a chance to offload or process these calls, the events may become problematic.

Without a peer support program in place, first responders may only have each other to lean on. The problem with this is it leaves first responders leaning on each other when they've all been through the trauma. The least capable person to help another person is someone who is just as traumatized as the rest. Often what happens in this situation is the designated "rock" in the group—the strong one who sucks it up to help the others—becomes the designated go-to for everyone else. The "rock" then pushes their feelings aside, never has a chance to recover themselves, and ends up hurting significantly more in the end.

One of my air medical programs sent a flight paramedic to me a few years ago on an emergency request. This medic arrived at his base one day and called his supervisor from his vehicle. He told her, "I can't set foot on the base, I can't take another flight, I can't treat another patient. I am done. I just can't do this anymore."

This medic arrived in my office two days later, completely defeated and hopeless. His issues were clear: he had a lot of bad calls he had not dealt with, and he was burned out. We got to work clearing his bad calls through the use of the technique called Eye Movement Desensitization and Reprocessing (EMDR), and we worked on restoring his resilience to combat his burnout through tangible goals and subsequent homework given by me to rebalance his life.

What also emerged in our time together was that this medic was also the "rock" at this base. Everyone would lean on him after bad calls, and he would stifle his own reactions to be present for others. We had a long talk about how unhealthy this was, and he returned to his base and addressed this with his colleagues. Everyone completely understood that having a designated "rock" basically crushes that "rock" under the pressure with no outlets for the designated "rock" to seek help. Instead, his base purposefully and deliberately redirected this practice to utilizing the peer support team that we had established in the organization.

Now, when I visit stations and bases, I frequently ask who the "rock" is. When I get the answer, I provide other options and resources. I explain that when I worked in the ER on weekend nights for ten years, many families that I worked with would designate a family member as the "strong one" or the "rock" to help them through a trauma or a death. I used to explain that if a family designated someone as the "rock," that family member would likely end up with ulcers, depression, delayed grief, or some sort of malady as the result of being the designated strong one. No one wants this, especially in the public safety world.

The other problem with only having the ability to lean on each other is that the culture at a specific agency may prohibit this. If an agency's culture is driven by the stigma associated with having normal reactions to horror, this will leave first responders to struggle and possibly flounder on their own. Embracing a culture that understands the struggles associated with dealing with awful events, eliminating the stigma of having normal reactions to trauma, and implementing an effective system for receiving help is the key. My book, *Smashing the Stigma and Changing the Culture in Emergency Services,* addresses this in depth.

The worst situations I have seen is leadership that promotes getting help but then punishes its personnel for doing just that. This leadership style is hypocritical, unsafe, and completely inappropriate. Personnel who exist in agencies with this kind of culture absolutely refuse to ask for help no matter how good the help is around them. The toxicity then perpetuates itself as the seasoned first responders warn the new hires to not ask for help. The result is that the overall health of the agency is in constant decline. It takes a change in leadership and several years to turn this nasty ship around. To me, this is the most frustrating thing leadership can do to first responders.

Most first responders at any given time do not have a therapist they can see, and the vast majority are definitely not willing to even call a therapist. Many first responders who have had bad experiences with therapists who do not understand public safety will not give therapy another try. With no real connection to the mental health world in many agencies, first responders are once again left to deal with things on their own or to lean on each other.

All of this is why we have peer support teams. Strong, well-run teams are seen by first responders as valuable resources. First responders can, will, and do speak to each other. They do lean on each other and having a peer support team allows them to lean on others who were not directly involved with the event. An objective, compassionate, knowledgeable, and nonjudgmental peer support team member who will listen, normalize, and assist is a life saver. The power in the process saves lives. I have seen this so many times in my career. First responders have told me time and again that they have no idea what they would have done without the peer support team.

One of my former patients, a firefighter, represents what it's like to survive an incident without a peer support program. Her boyfriend, also a firefighter, was significantly injured and burned during an explosion. My patient sucked it up for months as she cared for him in the hospital and later at home. She spent years watching over him, taking him to appointments and aiding him in the healing process. As she did this, she completely disregarded her own needs. She had great friends who helped her, but no peer support team. She was not only missing physical assistance for her exhausting circumstances; she was missing the education, normalization, and the pressure valve release that a well-trained peer support team could have provided for her. As she sat in my office and choked back tears in her first session, she told me that she felt shame and guilt for needing help, since she was not the one who was hurt. Through therapy, she was able to not only process the event, the aftermath, and her vicarious trauma, she also learned that her need for assistance was completely valid. She, like so many others I have worked with, would have really benefited from a trained peer support team.

My message to leadership that is on the fence about a peer support team is that you pay now or you pay later. First responders who begin to struggle after an event frequently call in sick, they are late for shifts, their performance declines, they garner complaints from the public, and they quit their jobs. To leaders who do not want to invest in peer support, I ask them to put a price on a struggling employee who declines for years and eventually is terminated or quits. In addition to those costs, add on the cost of hiring and training another employee. This budget drain is equivalent to years of sponsoring a peer support program, which could have possibly saved the careers of not just one, but a multitude of first responders. Pay now or pay later.

Chapter Two

Establish

*For a team to work, management has to get it and sup-
port it... at all levels. It ain't cheap, but it is so worth it.*

Dave
PHI Air Medical Peer Support Team

The first step in establishing a peer support program is to
identify the proper people to take the lead on this en-
deavor and to create the policies. Initially, a couple of
line personnel who are passionate about establishing a
team, along with an administrative person to provide the
support and push forward, is a good combination to
begin with. The line personnel do not necessarily need to
be trained in peer support just yet, although this may
help given the questions that typically arise and the
knowledge that good training provides. The administrative person is ideally someone who is also passionate
and supportive of a peer support program and has the
time to dedicate to the establishment of the team. I have
found that this person is often an assistant chief or director in charge of health and wellness.

Establish Peer Support Policies

The key to good policies is to keep them simple, direct, and comprehensive enough to give teams the latitude to function properly. Here are the elements of the best polices I have found. Consider this a sample, which any agency can adjust according to their needs. The best policies include sections on:

- Purpose
- Mission
- Goals
- Standard Operating Guidelines
- Peer Support Team Composition
- Activities
- Contact Guidelines
- Recruitment and Selection
- Confidentiality
- Social Media
- Training
- Budget

Purpose

A brief purpose statement is a nice option to give an understanding of what the policy is about. An example:

The purpose of this policy is to provide direction to the formation and implementation of an official Peer Support Team Policy Manual, to be accepted by the de-

*partment and utilized for the employees and family
members of the XYZ department.*

Mission

Again, the mission should be clear, concise, and straight-forward.

*Our mission is to provide XYZ Department per-
sonnel, both sworn and non-sworn, psychological and
emotional support through pre-incident education,
spousal/family support, on-scene support, and post-
incident support as needed.*

*The peer support team will be comprised of agen-
cy members who have been specially trained in peer
support techniques and work in conjunction with mental
health professionals who specialize in providing support
to emergency service personnel.*

Goals

The goals are listed to augment the mission statement.
Sample goals include:

1) *To provide a system of trusted support that will
aid employees in resolving situations affecting
their personal and professional environments.*

2) *To foster the physical, emotional, and social
health of employees.*

3) *To provide information about various aspects of*

peer support through educational materials and
resources.

4) To provide a liaison between the employee and
the department to identify and assist with resources available to them.

5) To develop and implement a peer support training program.

6) To work in conjunction with the peer support
teams of local and regional departments to promote cross-agency dissemination of training materials and opportunities and to establish working relationships with other public safety peer
support teams.

Standard Operating Guidelines

At this point, it is important for the policy to address
guidelines. At the start of the guidelines, it is a good idea
to restate the purpose so that the mission and intent are
clear. An example:

The purpose of the peer support program is to
prevent or lessen the potential negative impact of stress
upon employees by providing emotional support, information, and assistance.

The program will provide employees with psychological and emotional support through one-on-one discussions, pre-incident education, education on stress
management, spousal/significant other support, on-scene

support, and post-incident support.

The peer support team will be comprised of department members, of any rank or position, who have been specially trained in peer support and crisis intervention techniques. Team members will work in conjunction with designated mental health professionals. The peer support team is supported by the XYZ Department as "peer support team members."

Peer Support Team Composition

After the purpose portion of the standard operating guidelines, define the various roles of the team composition.

The peer support team will be made up of the following:

Assistant Chief of Operations: *The functions of the assistant chief are to:*
1) *Oversee the program.*
2) *Develop, advise, and approve program policy.*
3) *Approve funding for program activities including training, travel, and educational outreach.*
4) *Provide administrative support to the program.*
5) *Constitute a line of authority between the program, the clinical consultant, and the department.*
6) *Authorize membership into the program.*

12

7) *Authorize the activation of the team in large-scale events.*

8) *Approve all requests for assistance from outside agencies.*

Clinical Consultant: *The clinical consultant manages all matters related to the psychological or clinical aspects of the program. The clinical consultant will be a licensed health care professional in the State of XX affiliated with the department. The functions of the clinical consultant are to:*

1) *Consult and advise on all of the clinical aspects of the program.*

2) *Offer clinical support and guidance to the team leader.*

3) *Assist in securing relevant training and continuing education materials for the peer support team.*

4) *Assist in the development of policy and protocol.*

5) *Act as a liaison between the peer support team and other mental health professionals supporting the team.*

6) *Supervise and conduct peer support activities when necessary, under the direction of the Department.*

Peer Support Team Leader: *A team leader is a senior member of the peer support team. This position is not a* promoted position and department rank does not define who is eligible for the role of peer support team leader. The selection of the peer support team leader will be made by the peer support team members and the recommendation will be forwarded to the clinical consultant and the assistant chief for approval. Team leaders will be chosen based on reputation, leadership skills, and a willingness and desire to serve in this capacity. The functions of the team leader are to:

1) Manage the peer support team.
2) Assist the clinical consultant in deploying and implementing peer support activities.
3) Maintain records of team activities.
4) Facilitate recruitment of new members.
5) Assist the clinical consultant in disseminating educational material and developing training for the team.
6) Act as a Point of Contact (POC) for outside agencies requesting assistance with a critical incident or development of a peer support team.
7) Act as the POC for the chapter of the local union and to request their assistance with funding or resources as needed.
8) Act as a peer support team member in addition to these listed functions.

I strongly encourage peer support teams to have two team leaders. This allows for the availability of more than one team lead in the event that one of the team leaders is on duty and busy, out of town, or dealing with personal circumstances that prohibit a peer support response. Having two team leaders also helps mitigate burnout and fatigue associated with serving in this role. Trading off being the primary contact on responses gives each person the ability to disconnect from duties as needed.

Peer Support Team Member: *The peer support team members are the main providers and resource for employees seeking assistance. Their functions are to:*

1) *Provide crisis intervention and basic support for employees and their families.*
2) *Provide referrals to a mental health professional either through the Employee Assistance Program (EAP), available insurance providers, or other professional contacts following the process as defined in the Peer Support Policy Manual.*
3) *Triage and consult the clinical consultant in a crisis event and provide recommendations about what crisis intervention services are needed.*
4) *Assist in educating employees about peer support and psychological support services.*
5) *Assist in deploying and implementing peer support.*

Ideally, a peer support team should be 10 percent of the agency's population. Consider this number a goal or an eventual possibility in the beginning, because the initial team may be quite a bit smaller. When recruiting, think in terms of quality versus quantity (see Chapter Three for more information on recruitment). The activity, conduct, and professionalism of the peer support team in the first two years is vitally important. When a team operates well, maintains a steady focus on the mission, and displays compassion and professionalism, this will draw other employees to the team for future recruitment.

Activities

At this point in the policies, team member activities should be defined.

1) *The peer support program will consist of XYZ Department members who have successfully gone through the peer support program recruitment process.*

2) *Before being cleared to assist in peer support operations, each member will complete the peer support training and sign the Peer Support Agreement.*

3) *Peer support is not a substitute for professional counseling. Peer support team members are not trained mental health professionals and may not diagnose nor treat mental health conditions.*

4) *All peer support activities and contacts are voluntary. Employees may choose to utilize or re-*

ject peer support.

5) *Employees failing to meet department expectations, on a performance improvement plan, or on administrative leave during an investigation, will not participate in peer support activities as a peer support team member.*

Contact Guidelines

These guidelines supplement the activities portion of the policy. They are designed to further clarify how the team functions within a department and every employee's right to access or refuse peer support.

1) *Contact by peer support can never be forced on an individual.*

    a. *No order will be given by a superior for an employee to contact peer support. Suggestions may be made in good faith.*

    b. *Contacting peer support will never be a condition of a performance improvement plan.*

    c. *Contacting peer support will never be a condition of disciplinary action.*

2) *Interaction with a team member in the peer support capacity requires expressed consent by the individual.*

3) *Peer support team members may initiate contact with an individual on good faith for high-profile*

   incidents or requests by a third party.

    a. Contact will only consist of providing an individual the means to contact peer support if they desire to do so.

    b. Peer support will not release any information about an unsolicited contact. All inquiries will be addressed by stating that an individual was given the means to contact peer support if they desired to do so.

4) Peer support contact information will be provided to employees who:

   a. Sustain an on-the-job injury.

   b. Request FMLA.

   c. Request leave donation due to injury or illness.

   d. Are involved in an internal investigation.

   e. Are placed on administrative leave.

5) Peer support team members who feel an on-duty employee is a hazard to themselves or others will immediately contact the assistant chief of operations, or their designee, to request the employee be removed from operational status.

6) The shift commander should consider activating the peer support team for calls involving:

   a. Traumatic events involving children.

   b. Mass casualty incidents.

   c. Significant incidents involving department members or immediate families.

   d. Any unusual event with a powerful impact.

The shift commander will make the request to the team leader (or their designee). The team leader (or their designee) will be responsible for coordinating the response of the peer support team.

Inherent in this portion of the policy is the fact that during a crisis or a situation involving very personal circumstances of a first responder, peer support team members are able to function completely outside the chain of command and go directly to the administrative person in charge of the team as needed. An example is a situation where we had a first responder who was unsafe and needed to be hospitalized. The only person notified was the assistant chief of health and wellness because we needed the employee's FMLA paperwork requested from human resources. Due to confidentiality (see below), the assistant chief was not provided with any information regarding the situation, other than the fact that the paperwork was needed. As the team clinician, I was able to complete and submit the paperwork. Understandably, this type of situation requires a lot of trust and professionalism. This also highlights the importance of good policies and adherence to these policies. Leadership's willingness to work with the team and trust in the process allowed the employee to return to full duty successfully.

Recruitment and Selection

The next section addresses how team members are recruited and selected. This can include an application, an interview, and a letter of reference. If a team is in the infancy stages, the recruitment and selection can be done by the founding members (both the line personnel and the administrative person).

The addition of peer support team members will be done on an as-needed basis. Selections will be made from eligible candidates by current peer support team members.

Qualified individuals are:

- *Any sworn or non-sworn employee in good standing with the department.*
- *Not working under a performance improvement plan.*
- *Not currently the subject of an internal investigation.*

Confidentiality

Imperative to every policy is the confidentiality statement, which is the foundation for peer support. Confidentiality is granted through state policy or statutes. This is done on a state-by-state basis. I practice in two states. In Texas, the legal right for peer support team members to assure confidentiality is in the Health and Safety

Code. In Arizona, it is a statute. This should be researched prior to implementing policies.

The peer support team is a confidential program. It is of vital importance to the peer support team that a strong presence of trust is established and maintained among those who would seek our services. This requires understanding of our confidentiality policies by department administration, the clinical consultant, and all peer support team members.

1) *No records identifying employees who utilize the program will be maintained.*

2) *Peer support team members shall not discuss information obtained while acting in a peer support capacity without consent of the employee, with anyone other than the clinical consultant, other mental health professionals, or other peer support team members for the purpose of mental health support unless otherwise required by law.*

3) *Peer support team members shall not divulge shared information with other employees, family members, friends, supervisors or management, or the general public.*

4) *Peer support team members shall not be found insubordinate or otherwise in violation of city and/or department policy for failure to release or share information about an employee under internal investigation, obtained as a peer support team member, or acting in an official capacity, unless otherwise required by law.*

5) *Employees shall be advised that confidentiality will be maintained except as required in the following circumstances:*

    a. *The employee discloses information that leads the peer support team member to believe the employee is an imminent threat to themselves or others.*

    b. *The employee discloses information about suspected or alleged child abuse or elder abuse.*

    c. *The employee discloses information regarding legal issues that impact employment.*

    d. *Any other instances required by law.*

Social Media

This policy is the result of a lesson learned by a team member who posted condolences for the suicide of a firefighter in another agency that had just been announced. The time of the announcement was late—somewhere close to 2230. She posted condolences to the department on social media and went to bed. When she woke up the next morning, there were twenty or so "What happened?" type comments. People were upset that she was seen as being "in the know" because she is on peer support. While this section is not mandatory, I highly encourage adherence to something along these lines.

Due to the highly visible nature of social media, it is imperative that peer support team members maintain an image of leadership and confidentiality. Any breach, or perceived breach, of our ability to lead or maintain confidentiality would be detrimental to the peer support mission. Therefore, peer support team members will adhere to the following rules regarding social media:

1) If the peer support team is utilized in an incident involving an employee(s), the entire peer support team will refrain from any and all social media regarding the incident.

2) If there is an incident involving any other public safety agency, peer support team members shall not engage in any social media regarding the incident for **twenty-four hours** post official release.

3) Peer support team members shall refrain from making negative or derogatory comments toward the department or the peer support team on social media.

4) Peer support team members shall abide by the XYZ Department's social media policies that are already in place.

Training

The final element of the policy addresses the training for

team members. Training requirements can be adjusted based on the needs of the department and the team, and the feasibility of attending training with regard to schedules. Chapter Four will address training.

Training is paramount to the team's ability to effectively and with confidence interact with personnel seeking peer support.

1) *All new members will attend the peer support classes, in accordance with the clinical consultant, before engaging in any peer support team activities.*

2) *Continuing education will be provided at annual recurrent training and quarterly (or whenever deemed appropriate) QA/QI meetings. Team members are required to attend recurrent training each year to remain active. If they are unavailable during the scheduled recurrent training, they may meet with the clinical consultant individually to review the materials.*

I highly discourage starting a team without a policy in place. The policy provides structure and clear expectations. With a good policy, leadership can and will support the team, because they are aware of how the team operates. A good policy allows leadership to not only support the team, but also to step out of the way and trust the team to do their work.

In 2018, there was line-of-duty death of a K-9 officer in a rural county close to where I practice in Texas. This county is fairly sparse, with minimal resources to support a tragic event such as this one. The chief of the department reached out to me and asked for help. Specifically, he asked for peer support to assist on the day the death occurred. I called a chief at a local police department and a chief deputy at the local sheriff's office. After a two-sentence explanation of what happened and what I needed, I had the immediate green light to deploy peer support team members from these two agencies. Some of these team members were on duty and were replaced immediately so they could deploy. The communication with leadership that occurred in establishing the peer support teams, along with the clear policies, has created programs that operate so well, there is no pushback or questioning.

One of the first things I am always asked by fledgling teams is whether or not I have policies I can share. I am a firm believer that no one should recreate the wheel and go through the process of creating a policy when this program feels so new to everyone. Having policies established at the beginning of peer support team formation is paramount to the success of any program. Again, the policy I shared is a format that can be used and altered as needed.

Budget

To budget for a peer support program, it is important to plan for the various aspects of the needs of the team. The obvious budgetary item to tackle first is the training. Obtaining a quote from the chosen instructor and budgeting the cost to have the entire team present for training is the largest portion of the budget. When budgeting for training, also consider the cost to perform monthly or quarterly, semi-annual, or annual trainings or meetings based on how frequently the team can feasibly meet.

The next thing to budget for is the operational callouts. There is no way to predict how busy a team will be or how many times team members will be called out. Asking neighboring teams about their volume is a good way to start. The other thing to consider is whether or not peer support team members are being paid, strictly serving on a volunteer basis, or being allowed to flex their time as callouts happen. My customers use a variety of these three modes based on the resources they have. The one firm policy about callouts is that if a team member is called out for a crisis and spends the night before a regularly scheduled shift awake because they are dealing with the event, they are not expected to be on duty the next day. Being called out all night is considered their duty time and a replacement for this person is assigned. This is a safety issue, and I always address this with leadership in every department as we start a new team.

The final budget items are the supplies. Team shirts, a budget for water, food, sweatpants to change out of a soiled uniform that is considered evidence, etc., are all things that should be budgeted for. Given the fact that everyone in a crisis is at the base of Maslow's Hierarchy of Needs (see Chapter Four), these comfort items are essential to the operations of the team. I ask departments to budget $500 a year for these.

Chapter Three

Recruit

Being part of peer support has been incredible. When someone feels safe enough to share their struggles and be vulnerable with me, it's a tremendous compliment. The moment our peers realize just how much we're willing to meet them with only empathy and compassion, they truly start to feel better and that's what this is about, taking care of each other. The best part is witnessing the weight come off their shoulders and feeling their relief. What a gift.

Laci
PHI Air Medical Peer Support Team

Recruiting team members is the next process to take place. This is a monumentally important process, because the team members any agency chooses for peer support will be the make or break of the program. This is especially true in the first years of a peer support team, when the process is either being accepted and ingrained into a culture or it's not. The behaviors of the team members are being watched by everyone. The team can become something that is an automatic thought and go-to resource when something happens, or it can become a joke that is never utilized.

The demographics of your team should be as diverse as possible and represent every aspect of your agency. I encourage teams that I establish to include line personnel and supervisors up to a sergeant level in law enforcement, and a lieutenant or captain in the fire service/EMS. I prefer that the team is composed of both younger and newer first responders, as well as the more seasoned personnel. I want the team to have a good mixture of race, gender, sexual orientation, and religious backgrounds. In other words, we are training a team full of people that any first responder can approach and be comfortable with, based on the issues they are dealing with. I also require that the team be composed of dispatchers, administrative people who take care of the agency, and any other occupation represented in the department.

The profile of the team member that I look for is not the perfect person who has had the perfect career. While this person really doesn't truly exist in any agency, leadership tends to want to choose employees who have been easy to manage and who have not been problematic to supervisors or to the agency. Because these employees are generally easy to work with, they tend to be chosen automatically for peer support. The characteristics of a good team member is a mixture of both amazing and rough around the edges.

When I assist with recruiting for peer support, I look for team members who are natural-born leaders.

These are the public safety people who others gravitate toward for advice, words of wisdom, and guidance. I am looking for mature, kind, and open-minded individuals who do not judge their colleagues. I am also looking for first responders who, even during the darkest times, generally do not badmouth or disparage their agencies.

Beyond that, I want team members who have overcome adversity. I want the officer who has been involved in a shooting, the paramedic who made a medical error, the firefighter who was trapped in a basement during a house fire, and the dispatcher who has worked terrible incidents. The key is that these individuals have healed in whatever sense they know how to and now have the wisdom to share with others. In other words, they are resilient. Maybe they went to therapy, but maybe they didn't. Maybe they relied on friends, family, or their faith to get them through. The ideal team member made some mistakes along the way in their healing— they drank too much, fought with their spouse, alienated their children—but they learned. Maybe they learned the hard way, but the bottom line is they achieved some wisdom along the way. As I said earlier, wisdom is hard-earned and causes gray hair. But wisdom makes us better human beings who want to help others not step into the pitfalls that we have. Wisdom causes us to want to help circumvent the pain that others may face.

With the younger and newer team members, they may not have the experience base that the seasoned first responders have. However, there are many younger public safety professionals who, because of their histories, bring a level of wisdom to the table for peer support. Perhaps it was their childhood or something that occurred in the academy that resulted in this wisdom. Whatever it is, we want to tap into that when recruiting younger team members. When a young first responder wants to work through the frustrations of being a rookie or a booter, there is no one better to talk to than a person who is just a few years ahead of them who can still very much relate to that experience.

The other very important trait I look for when recruiting team members is the ability to keep one's mouth shut. If someone is known to spread rumors or share secrets, I will eliminate them from the list. With confidentiality, we are looking for the person who will not share the team activities, what happens during an activation, or what is going on with a particular person. This is massively important, and I cannot stress this enough. One of my agencies established a peer support team many years ago and recruited the wrong people. The gossip started and the team ended—for TEN years. This is how long it took to rebuild the trust and interest in the process at both the line and leadership levels. The new team members on this rebuilt team are some of the most tight-lipped people I have had the pleasure of working with.

Some pitfalls of recruiting tend to be just sloppy ways of managing the recruiting process. The first is when someone in a leadership role puts their problematic employee on the team because they are hoping that going through the training will somehow help them. I explain to leadership that this is wasting a seat in the class. Spending three tough days of training with me does not "fix" your problem child. As a matter of fact, that training might trigger some things and make the situation worse for this person. I don't have a magic aura that somehow changes people just by being around me. Training for peer support is not a substitute for the therapy needed by someone who is struggling desperately.

Another pitfall is the recruiting process. I have noticed that many agencies, especially in the fire service, use a survey that they send out to the entire department, and everyone essentially picks who they think would be good at peer support. This becomes more of a popularity contest than a process to understand the true intentions of people who express an interest in peer support, which is what the interview process should be. The other issue with a survey is that it puts pressure on those who are picked to be on the team, when it's possible they don't have the desire, time commitment, or the mental energy to do this type of work. If a department picks a much-loved and respected first responder to be on the team, it's possible that person has not told anyone that they are going through a contentious divorce, an awful custody battle, or are in the midst of caring for aging parents. Departments that use the survey say that they give anyone chosen the ability to turn the peer support role down, but what if the chosen one has a hard time saying no? This may be clearly not the right time in someone's life to be on peer support, but if they feel obligated and join the team, we end up with a member who is rarely available and is stressed and distracted.

Peer support requires resilience. We need the most resilient people who have a passion for helping others to step up. Typically, we are asking for a two-year commitment unless a person's circumstances change and they are no longer able to provide this service. We are looking for team members who will step up and be ready. I explain that the incidents are rarely on Tuesday at 1100 when everyone is available. The events are at 0230, on Christmas Eve, during the Super Bowl, and when half the team is on duty, leaving the other half to manage the situation. Out of the half that are off duty, someone is always out of town, dealing with a sick child, or otherwise unavailable. That leaves the few who are available to leave their homes during the Super Bowl or Christmas Eve dinner to go help their colleagues. Peer support requires resilience. Peer support requires commitment.

The Application Process

To begin recruiting, I typically generate an email that describes the functions and roles of peer support team members. I address the upcoming training, with dates already established to avoid confusion. I make the expectations of the members and the team as clear as possible, and I highlight the importance of being with people on the worst days of their lives. I then attach an application to this email, and send it to the director, chief, or sheriff of the department so that they can add their own words to stress the importance of the team and forward it to the entire department.

The application has a deadline, and I also request a letter of recommendation from a supervisor or a colleague. Here is the information I typically request on an application:

- *Name*
- *Phone (Mobile)*
- *Phone (Work)*
- *Email*
- *Employee Number*
- *Current Position*
- *Please describe your interest in being on the peer support team.*
- *What personal and/or professional qualities do you have that would benefit the peer support team?*
- *Have you been involved in a critical incident? If so, please describe how you recovered or worked through the incident to get past it.*
- *Do you have the flexibility to respond to an employee who is experiencing an extreme crisis?*

While the applications are simple, the answers are extremely important. The time, energy, and passion given to each answer is very telling about the applicant's commitment and desire to serve in this capacity.

In addition to the application, the reference letter should be sent in as a packet. The contents of the letter are all part of the big picture. This is where we get a sense of reliability and responsibility, as well as commitment to the process.

Finally, I recommend doing a thorough interview. A valuable use of time is sitting down with candidates and asking them to share their history and the reasons they want to join peer support, as well as what their expectations are and really discussing their availability. As interviewees finish the interviews, a clear picture usually emerges of who this person is and how they will operate on a team.

One of the most notable interviews I did was when I was assisting US Airways (before they merged with American Airlines) establish their peer support team. This was in the aftermath of flight 1549, or the "Miracle on the Hudson," when the aircraft struck a flock of birds after taking off from JFK Airport in New York City and the pilots had to ditch the aircraft in the Hudson River. Due to the aftermath of this event, one of the three flight attendants on the aircraft that day decided the airline needed a peer support program.

Because US Airways had four bases, we traveled to each base to conduct the interviews. What we found along the way were some amazing flight attendants who joined the team and some who looked good on paper but presented very differently in person. Some that we thought looked amazing on the applications were not appropriate for the peer support team.

During our time in Philadelphia, I met an amazing flight attendant whose name is Bill. I asked Bill about the worst thing he had experienced and how he dealt with it, to which I received the reply that left my jaw hanging.

Bill told me that he was a flight attendant on flight 1493 on February 1, 1991. This flight was on final approach to LAX (Los Angeles) when a distracted air traffic controller landed them right behind and into SkyWest flight 5569. As the two planes collided, they became a mass of metal, fire, and momentum. They skidded off the runway onto the tarmac, where they came to an eventual stop as a fiery ball of flames. Everyone on the SkyWest plane died, and half of the passengers as well as half of the crew members on the US Airways flight died.

Bill proceeded to tell me about evacuating, saving passengers by pulling them out of the aircraft, the eventual intervention of other passengers who sat him down because he was so badly injured, his survivor guilt because the flight attendant sitting next to him died, his recovery process, and his eventual return to flying. Needless to say, Bill was brought onto the team, and he ended up being the team leader for the Philadelphia base. Bill's story can be found on the TV show, *Why Planes*

Crash, featured on the Weather Channel.

I share this story to highlight the importance of the interview process and also to share some wisdom about the process, which is to be ready for anything!

The Team Clinician

Finding the right clinician to guide and train the peer support team can be arduous. If a team does not have an established relationship with a clinician, it is best to recruit a clinician based on word of mouth from others. The key is to find a clinician who is passionate about first responders and believes in the peer support process. This person ideally has ridden along with first responders for multiple shifts, is in tune with the terminology of the first responder world and is available for callouts and events as they happen. This person must also be reliable and dependable for the team members to call for guidance when in a bind.

The clinician should be ready to both attend training with the new team and then to implement ongoing training. There are considerable responsibilities associated with this role, so the right amount of commitment along with good experience is the key to success.

The bottom line when it comes to recruiting is to take your time and get it right. The team composition is of utmost importance. As a therapist, I often say that 95 percent of my work is the human relationship I establish with my patients. This is very true for peer support. When horrible things happen, your first responders want genuine, kind, trustworthy people with legitimate credentials to show up. They don't want people they can't trust.

Chapter Four

Train

Tania always said all through the class that we needed to be ready. About one week after training, I answered the call for a peer in need. He was a friend and coworker. I arrived, and our team helped him for the next three weeks. Our team did a great job with the whole family. What I remember the most was driving home at the end of the activation. I had to stop and process all we had done. I just wanted to shout that after twenty-nine years of service, I was now sure that I truly helped and made a difference.

Gary
Williamson County Sheriff's Office Peer Support Team

The initial training for a peer support program is extremely important. The training should educate the team members thoroughly and arm them with the tools and skills to begin this work. This is an overview of the training I provide. Again, it can be modified to fit the needs of any agency.

My initial peer support training is three days. The mornings of each day are spent on content and teaching concepts, with the afternoons reserved for group activities and practicing skills and scenarios. I do this on purpose—generally students are more focused in the mornings and battling fatigue after lunch and throughout the afternoon. Therefore, I keep the mornings focused on presentations and content, and I keep my students moving in the afternoons.

The training to be able to make the biggest impact possible in each situation is the most inspiring part for me.

Michael
Glendale Fire Department Peer Support Team

Day One Morning Content

After introductions and a discussion about the role of peer support, I go over the policies with the team leaders assisting me. I want to establish their role as team leaders and lay the groundwork for operational expectations. The reasons I go over policy first are because it is dry content and everyone is typically very focused during the morning of the first day, and also because if the policies are not discussed first, everyone will begin asking questions related to the policies by mid-morning. So, policies first.

The next thing I teach the class is the importance of adhering to Maslow's Hierarchy of Needs during any crisis. I show them the hierarchy and explain that everyone in a crisis goes to the base of the hierarchy. In explaining this, I assure the team that they will not have the magic power to take people's pain away, or even the magic words to reassure someone that everything will be all right because such things do not exist. Instead, in a crisis moment, handing someone a bottle of water and making sure they get home safely is not only what they need, it's where we start. I ask students to put themselves in the shoes of someone else and to think about what they need at the time. I explain to the team that if they do this, they will never go wrong.

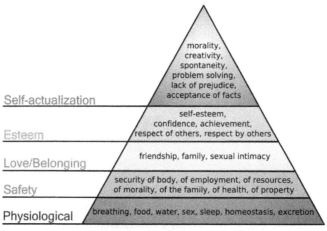

Maslow's Hierarchy of Needs

The next portion of my class addresses very important information regarding the fight-or-flight response and the link between fight or flight and the four types of stress. I wrote about the importance of education in my first book, *First Responder Resilience: Car-*

ing for Public Servants. The educational brief discussed in Chapter Two of that book is what I address at this point in my peer support classes. The difference is that I am now going much more in depth, asking my students to retain the information thoroughly, ask questions, and commit this information to long-term memory. I explain to them that in a crisis, when fellow first responders have these reactions, it is imperative that the team members can normalize and explain why these things are occurring. In the midst of a crisis, everyone needs to know they are normal. If first responders are not validated, this leads to shame, self-doubt, and guilt. Education and normalization are the key. I continuously quiz my students on these concepts throughout the three days.

Below is the educational piece on fight or flight and the four types of stress from *First Responder Resilience: Caring for Public Servants.*

> The place to start in a stress/trauma brief is normalizing the stress response by linking it to the fight-or-flight response that's ingrained in all of us. Every public safety professional understands this concept and when the four types of stress are connected to the fight-or-flight response, it normalizes and validates all their reactions. This is how to grab their attention and keep it. We all need the fight-or-flight response to survive. It is the awesome, kick-butt, and amazing human response that allows us to do things we never

thought we could. When you set fight or flight at the foundation of stress, it removes the whole "touchy feely" weakness climate that often exists in stress briefs and turns off your audience.

In a fight-or-flight response, our brain activates our bodies to produce copious amounts of adrenaline, glucose, and cortisol. This response is all about strength, lasting in the fight, and blocking pain—it is all about survival and nothing else. The difference between fight and flight is a choice your brain makes. If you are walking in the woods and a mama bear, who happens to be spending a nice day with her cub, would like to speak with you, you are not going to fight with her. It's time to go! One of my SWAT teams told me they thought flight meant cowardice. The choice to flee has nothing to do with cowardice; sometimes the best choice for survival is to retreat and re-attack when backup arrives. Your brain is making a good decision— kill now, kill later, or be killed. It's really quite simple.

After acknowledging this basic foundation of the stress reaction, it's imperative to link fight or flight as a common thread in the four types of stress: acute stress, delayed stress, cumulative stress, and post-traumatic stress disorder.

Acute stress is also called incident-prompted stress. It begins on-scene, or within twenty-four hours, and is very obvious because there are many physiological reactions that are overt and uncomfortable. Acute stress responses occur after responders are involved in an overwhelming incident, their coping mechanisms are overwhelmed, and they have launched into fight or flight. There are a series of normal reactions evident with acute stress responses, and it's important that the normalization of these reactions is consistently mentioned. Signs of acute stress responses include:

Shaking—the cortisol triggers your circulation to divert your blood flow to your body's core in order to oxygenate the heart, lungs, and major muscles in your back, arms, and legs for running power and striking power. This is called shunting. Also, with decreased circulation, you are less likely to bleed to death if you are cut during a fight. When you couple shunting with adrenaline raging through your system, the side effect is shaking or trembling.

Throwing up—when you launch into fight or flight, you stop digesting because digestion burns too many calories that can be used for the fight. You don't need the food in your belly, so your system triggers you to get rid of it. Also, if you offload the weight in your belly, you are lighter so you can run faster.

Loss of bladder and bowel control—if your bladder is punctured or your bowel is eviscerated and the urine or feces go all over you, the long-term issue is that you will go septic. Your brain instructs your body to get rid of this possible health threat.

Prefrontal cortex shutdown—when your heart rate jumps to 180 to 220 beats per minute, it triggers your prefrontal cortex to shut down. This is the thinking, reasoning, analyzing, decision-making, and standard-operating-procedure-remembering portion of your brain. When that shuts off, the midbrain kicks on: this is the animal portion in all of us—kill or be killed. So, we kill.

Delayed stress is basically an acute stress reaction that occurs days, weeks, or even months after an event. The reason for the delay is because we "numb out" really well and take control during an incident. When the numbing wears off or the brain is ready to deal with it, responders and military members are punched with a delayed stress reaction. The delayed stress reaction is disturbing because it feels as though it comes out of nowhere. People who experience delayed stress reactions often think they are fine—good to go—and then, BAM! I always encourage folks to understand that this is normal and it's simply now time to deal with the event. The key is to reach out for help and take that help.

Cumulative stress is burnout. The key to managing burnout is to stay healthy and have a life outside the job. Stay hydrated, nourished, and rested. Take care of family and financial issues. Get regular check-ups. Keep your faith, friends, hobbies, and fun in your life, and not just your work friends, but all others. Step out of your comfort zone: attend church, go to your kids' school plays, and cheer them on at their baseball games! In other words, have balance in life. First responders with healthy balance are less likely to experience burnout and are generally more resilient.

Post-traumatic stress disorder is at the farthest end of the spectrum of the stress continuum and most public safety professionals fear that it will end their careers. It is extremely important to explain PTSD simply and clearly and address options for recovery. Here is the explanation I give in my briefs, and while this is simplified and condensed, the most important thing is to normalize this syndrome and provide hope that things can and will improve.

PTSD is the end result of exposure to a stress trauma so extreme it is beyond human coping capacity. This response and its severity are different for everyone. For example, two individuals may have experienced the same trauma and one will indicate it was the worst thing he has ever seen, while the other states it was no big deal. It boils down to interpretation and what your brain considers traumatic.

You take in information through your five senses; what you see, hear, taste, touch, and smell enter the frontal lobe of your brain. Normal information gets processed across the synapses in your brain and downloaded into your memory—short term or long term—depending on relevance.

Trauma and traumatic information get stored in your frontal lobe, which acts as a firewall for trauma and does not allow your brain to process it—it's simply too overwhelming.

Over time, your frontal lobe attempts to push the information into your memory, but if it's too traumatic, it simply can't do so without assistance.

As your frontal lobe attempts to download the traumatic memory, it causes the individual to re-experience the event over and over again. Each time this happens, it causes distress and a subsequent fight-or-flight response.

Over time, the fight-or-flight response happens so many times that the cortisol it produces crosses the blood-brain barrier and hijacks the limbic system.

Cortisol causes the hippocampus, which manages trauma and loss, to shrink.

When the hippocampus shrinks, the amygdala essentially becomes hijacked by the damage to the brain. The amygdala is the gatekeeper to the fight-or-flight reaction. This mechanism decides when it's time to set the survival response in motion and when everything is fine and safe. When the amygdala is damaged, it always defaults to fight or flight rather than safe because otherwise we would not survive during danger.

When the amygdala is damaged and defaults to fight or flight, it is no longer able to understand that you're fine. A car backfiring takes you right back to that firefight you were in. It doesn't care about logic. There is no timeline in the limbic system. All it knows is danger and how to set you in motion to stay alive.

PTSD is essentially your survival mechanism in the wrong loop or cycle.

The hippocampus is very "plastic." It heals by generating new neural pathways, and this is how we conquer PTSD. There are very effective techniques to realign the limbic system by opening these neural pathways. My favorite happens to be Eye Movement Desensitization and Reprocessing (EMDR).

I explain EMDR in-depth to my peer support classes.

Throughout the entire class, I give examples of events that I have worked to solidify the concepts. Adults learn well by tying a concept to an example. The stories I use are typically not easy to hear. I do this for two reasons. I want to prepare my class for the worst possible scenarios and to boost their confidence in understanding that no matter how awful the situation is, they can and will start to make a difference in the lives of first responders. The second reason I tell difficult stories is to assess where the team members are emotionally. My goal is to desensitize them to hearing tough stories over the three days, and also to tap into any unresolved issues they need to address as they embark on their peer support role.

The next portion of the class covers more signs and symptoms of both traumatic and day-to-day stress. I break them down into four categories: physical, cognitive, emotional, and behavioral. Again, giving examples of each concept to solidify the concepts in the minds of the students is imperative.

The final section of this portion of the class addresses resilience and stress management. I teach students how to teach others to restore their resilience and practice self-care. I explain to the team members that this is part of every activation or intervention. Explaining, teaching, and reminding first responders about self-care is the one absolute common thread in every activation.

Day One Afternoon Content

In the afternoon on day one, I quiz students returning from lunch (as a group) on the content covered in the morning. I then move into confidentiality. At this point, we review what confidentiality means, the importance of maintaining confidentiality, and what this looks like in terms of interactions with other peers on the team and colleagues who are not on the team. We review the limits of confidentiality: threats to harm self or others; child or elder abuse; and criminal activity that would get a person terminated from employment at the agency.

We then break into groups of two or three, and I

allow the students to practice explaining the confidentiality statement. This statement includes what confidentiality means, as well as what the limits are. I ask them to practice it on each other until it is smooth and comprehensive. I explain that the first few times a peer support student practices the statement, it feels like a Geraghty or Miranda warning. Most students fully agree that the smooth delivery of the confidentiality statement takes practice so that it's not off-putting and choppy.

The next portion of the class addresses empathy. I ask students to break into groups of four or five people and to congregate in these groups. I then present a scenario to the group and ask them to participate in the activity.

The scenario is that they are all emergency room personnel of equal rank. One day, a horrible accident occurred and they receive five patients with the exact same injuries (it does not matter what the injuries are). Due to hospital budget shortfalls, there is only one piece of equipment that all five patients need in order to survive. Each group must reach consensus as to who will survive, as the other four will die. I go on to explain consensus, which means everyone must agree, as a group, on the group's choice. Senior rank among the group members, arm-wrestling strength, or any other mode by which they might push through a nonconsensus decision does not count.

I then present the students with their five patients: a Catholic priest, a known terminally ill patient, a mother of three, a ten-year-old girl, and a physician who is on the verge of discovering the cure for cancer. I ask the groups to reach consensus and when they do, to then appoint a spokesperson for the group to discuss how they reached consensus.

Sometimes the groups take very little time to reach consensus, but others result in lengthy discussions and much negotiating to reach an agreement. Occasionally I have to give a group a two-minute and one-minute warning when they are struggling to reach a decision. What emerges from the students consistently in every class I teach is a sense of discomfort and agitation among the team members. As we go around to each group and ask what their decision was and how they reached consensus, there is a clear sense of questioning why we did this.

After each group has spoken, I explain the purpose of the activity. In trauma with first responders, the events are never perfect, nor are they pretty. These are the worst days of people's lives. In trauma, first responders are often backed into a corner and forced to make very difficult decisions that no one wants to have to make.

I highlight this by sharing a story about a van full of children that t-boned a pickup truck in the middle of an intersection in southern Travis County, Texas in 1995. It turned out to be a terrible mass casualty incident involving multiple children. When I explain the decisions that the paramedics from Austin-Travis County EMS had to make that day, suddenly the students begin to understand.

I go on to explain that as a peer support team member, they may be one of the few people in a first responder's life who hears and understands the entire story. They will likely be one of the very few people who does not second guess or judge the actions of the first responder. I go on to ask the class, "Don't we all need someone in our corner who understands us, who will listen to us, and who won't judge us on the worst days of our lives?"

At this point I see the light turn on in every student's eyes. Suddenly they are in tune with the gravity of their role as a peer support team member. They fully embrace the importance of their commitment to stepping up for their colleagues. They also begin to understand the burden they may carry in this role.

We finish day one with the students learning how to listen. I explain that first responders in emergency situations typically garner just enough information to make a very fast decision to mitigate a crisis. I explain that in the peer support role, I need them to slow down, sit on their hands, not rush to fix things, and to listen.

I have the students break again into groups of two or three, and I ask them to take turns telling each other a story. I direct them to make it a fun or cool story about a call, their kids, their pets, an adventure, or a funny thing that happened to them. The person who is in the listening role can do just that—listen. At the end of the story, the person who is listening is asked to recall as much information as they can remember about the story. What they find is that they recall a lot. I explain to the students that this activity is designed to train their brain to listen and also to train their brain what it feels like to really listen. I explain that when they listen to listen versus listening to respond, they get a much clearer picture of what a fellow first responder is going through. This, in turn, creates much better interventions, which is what we begin to cover on day two.

As we discuss listening, I also highlight the importance of silence. During training, peer support team members find themselves wanting to fill silence with words. I explain that a person who becomes silent is frequently processing what has occurred, feeling emotions, collecting their thoughts, and figuring out what they want to say next. If a peer support person interrupts this, it causes disruption in all of the things going on in the contact's (the person they are helping) mind. I train peer support team members to give the silence at least twenty seconds. If the contact does not say anything by that time, I ask team members to summarize what they have just said or validate or normalize the issues they are discussing. This is a nice way to pick up where the contact has left off to allow them to discuss it further, ask questions, or move forward with the next thing they want to say.

My peer support teams leave day one exhausted. My job as their trainer is not to fill them with fluff, daisies, and unicorns. My job is to get them ready for anything and everything, to include the worst-case scenario.

Day Two Morning Content

The first thing we do in the morning of day two is review the content of day one. I again provide new and different examples of experiences I have had to solidify the concepts. There is time for questions and review of anything that needs clarification.

From there we dive into interventions. The thing I explain first is that every situation involving more than one person must be triaged effectively to assure that the appropriate people are involved in the appropriate interventions at the right time.

From my first book, *First Responder Resilience: Caring for Public Servants,* this is how I explain triaging.

> The first step in providing interventions is to triage the involved personnel and to constantly reevaluate based on what has occurred. The act of triaging is one of the most important components in service delivery. You cannot respond to any critical incident or disaster without it. Caring for people is not a one-size-fits-all service. Understanding who needs what and when is imperative. Without good triaging, you are setting up the response plan for total failure, potentially

harming your employees. It is simply unacceptable.

Public safety folks who are in the midst of chaos have a very different experience and mindset after an incident than those who arrive later. The most frequent mistake made by clinicians and peer support teams who respond to incidents is that they get in a hurry and decide to use one or two interventions for everyone. The result is that responders who were directly impacted are placed into the same intervention as responders who arrived later, when the situation was under control. The intervention thus fails all of the participants. Rescuers who are severely traumatized are not interested in hearing from someone who had a minimal role.

The first thing I explain to teams is never, ever to be in a hurry. There is no reason to rush. Take the time to get your fingers on the emotional pulse of everyone involved. It will give you a feel of what to do and when to do it. Take the time to meet everyone and get a really good brief on what actually happened (not what you saw on the news). Get a sense of how the organizations involved are responding, including to the fact that help has arrived.

Once you are ready to start triaging and implementing intervention, make sure you keep it simple. I like to use a target analogy, with a bull's-eye in the middle and rings surrounding the bull's-eye.

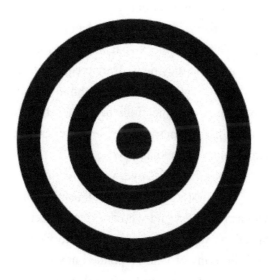

In the center of the bull's-eye are the first responders who were directly involved. This means the ones who were right there when it happened or were the first to arrive. In the event that those who were in the bull's-eye are deceased or seriously injured, the bull's-eye will include those who were first on the scene. If responders are seriously injured, their mental health care must begin as soon as reasonable or possible but may have to be delayed until physical recovery is underway.

Communications specialists involved in the incident are always in the bull's-eye. Never make the mistake of thinking that just because they were not present, they are fine or less impacted. Communications personnel can be just as traumatized, if not more so, than personnel on scene. They have no visual references and rely solely on what they hear. They create pictures in their minds. The overwhelming emotional experience for communications personnel, therefore, is utter helplessness, an experience extremely damaging to the human psyche.

From the bull's-eye, you move to the first ring. The first ring consists of team members who arrived next and who are often directly impacted, as well. As you move out to each ring, think in terms of who responded next, who was on duty at the time and, while they heard about it, they did not respond. And finally, personnel who were off duty at the time.

As you identify the personnel that fall into each area of the target, you can begin to plan your interventions based on what each group needs. The key to good triaging is this: While you can't always prevent the blurring of some of the lines, it is important to keep the groups with similar or homogeneous experiences as separate as possible. This means that it is imperative not to debrief personnel in the bull's-eye together with personnel who were off duty. Their experiences are drastically different, as are the ranges of reactions. Once you have a good sense of folks involved and their level of exposure, it is time to implement interventions.

Once we have covered triaging, we spend the rest of the morning on how to conduct one-on-one interventions. In introducing one-on-ones to the class, I explain that whether it's a personal or a professional issue, the model for conducting this type of intervention is flexible and comprehensive so that it can be used for any issue.

Assessment

At the very start of every one-on-one intervention is the assessment phase. This is when peer support members are listening. I explain to them that a typical 911 call that first responders engage in every day garners just enough information to make a decision. I refer to this as a "stick figure." A stick figure means a sketch of a situation, whether it's a crime that has occurred or a very sick patient that needs to be transported to the hospital. I ask peer support students to think in terms of having a Mona Lisa versus a stick figure painted in their minds before they begin to give input in their interventions. In other words, get a comprehensive view of what is going on with someone first.

In the assessment phase, the peer support member is listening and asking for clarification to help them fully understand what is occurring with the contact. Many times, during the assessment phase, as a contact is processing what has occurred, they begin to organize their thoughts, prioritize what they need to do to stabilize a situation, and clarify any other concerns. Simultaneously, a peer support team member who is listening well will be doing exactly the same thing.

From there, I address the obstacles to having a clear picture of the issue at hand. We address overthinking, escaping, avoiding, and enmeshment with others as potential pitfalls to clarity on any problem. As peer support members help the contact obtain clarity by listening and guiding them through a discussion, the contact will often begin to see things differently.

Intervention

We then address the process of intervention. I explain that every issue has three parts: the information, the interpretation, and the reaction. The information is the who, what, when, where, and how—the event, situation, or story. The details of the information are what paints the Mona Lisa for the peer support member.

From there we look at the contact's interpretation of the event. A person's interpretation depends on their history, perspective, prior experience, previous successful resolution of situations or problems, and their training. We explore thinking errors, or defense mechanisms, and how those play a role in the contact's interpretation. I then teach the students how to gently confront possible thinking errors to assist the contact in looking at the bigger picture or seeing things in a different light.

Finally, we address the reaction, which is another term for feelings. I joke that the "f word" is feelings, and I explain to students that the words *respond* and *react* are far less off-putting for first responders than the word *feel*. I also explain to students that the contact will frequently identify how they feel in the words they use without peer support even asking. But the phrase, "How does that make you feel?" will only shut the contact down.

I explain that feelings are actually logical and predictable. If one examines the information (the what) and the individual's interpretation of the information, how they react or feel about a situation makes perfect sense.

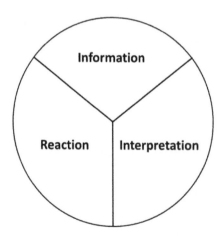

Taking Action

After this, we address how to take action. This is the answer to the "But what do we do?" question that all students have. I first explain that the factors that influence problem management are varied and ultimately have nothing to do with the peer support team member. Instead, they have everything to do with the contact. The factors that influence problem management include things like motivation to change, willingness to take risks, tolerance of human differences, attitude, commitment to finding a solution, and their degree of interest in solving the issue. I explain to peer support members to always remember that they are there as a guide or a catalyst to help create change, but ultimately the change has to be done by the contact.

There are three modalities to taking action. The first is the nondirective approach and is used the majority of the time. The nondirective approach means that the contact presents the problem or issue and the peer support member, after summarizing their understanding of the issue, asks the contact what their options are. At this point, the contact is able to list options and the order in which to do them.

The second modality is the cooperative approach. When the peer support team member asks the contact what their options are and the contact cannot think of any, the peer support member then begins to address possible options. They are more involved with helping the contact develop a plan and organizing the process to carry out the plan.

The final modality is the least used—the directive approach. This is reserved for the crisis or when someone is in danger. If a first responder expresses the desire to harm themselves, then peer support is taking them to a hospital. This approach is very direct and will involve other team members and the clinical consultant for backup.

I then teach the students how to help the contact make a list of goals, objectives to reach those goals, a plan of action, and a follow-up contact plan between the peer support member and the contact.

Throughout all of this portion of the class, I am using very specific examples to solidity the concepts. This is extremely important to do, as this is a very new skill for most peer support team members.

Day Two Afternoon Content

The afternoon of day two is spent practicing one-on-one interventions. The students make their mistakes (the classroom is the best place to make mistakes), build their skills, and improve their listening. We go from smaller problems to more significant events and issues as the afternoon progresses. I strongly encourage students to stay focused, challenge each other, and learn from as many mistakes as possible during this valuable training time.

We finish day two with the students doing a one-on-one with me. It's more of a peer support team-on-one because they participate as a group. For this exercise, I introduce the "pause button," which I let them know I will push every so often to check in with the students. After each check-in, I will push the "play button" to continue.

I proceed to share with the class an experience I had after Hurricane Katrina. It was in the immediate aftermath of my time in New Orleans. The class is aware from my introductory remarks on day one that Katrina was a very difficult, extended deployment for me. This event occurred as I was doing some work in Houston about two weeks after I returned from Katrina. I was still rundown and not super excited about traveling again, but I had an obligation to the customer.

I went for a run that morning because the hotel gym was closed. It was about 0500 and still dark, and I was running on trails near a ravine. At one point I heard a male yell, "Hey" and quickly realized that I was being chased by five young adult males. It was clear their intentions were not good. At first I tried to ignore them, hoping if I did they would leave me alone. When this did not work, I turned to face them as they ran toward me, preparing to fight them. I then realized how large they were and knew that once I was on the ground, I had zero chance of winning this fight.

As I relate this story during training, the intensity

in listening for each student is clear. So is the fact that they are holding their breath. Generally, at two points I will hit the pause button and check in. I ask the males if they are uncomfortable and wonder if they would refer me to a female peer support person, and we discuss the fact that they need to have the Mona Lisa painted in their minds before they make any decisions. I remind the entire class that no matter what, they need to breathe.

I then finish the story. As soon as I knew I could not fight these men, I made a choice. Rather than being dragged away and picked apart by savages, I chose to take matters into my own hands. After all, my life would never be the same if they got what they wanted. So, I chose to end my life. I decided to step off the running trail and get hit by a vehicle. As a matter of fact, I chose the vehicle and planned to dive right through the windshield. The perpetrators realized this was going to bring a lot of attention to them, so they stopped. One of them called me a "crazy bitch" before they turned around and ran away. At this point I hurried back to the trail, as traffic narrowly missed me. A Houston police officer witnessed me in the road and as soon as I saw the flashing red and blue lights I breathed a sigh of relief. He told me that the description of the men matched some suspects who were evacuees and were on a crime spree in Houston. An off-duty firefighter ran by on the trail. He stopped to see what was going on and thankfully ran with me back to my hotel. I got ready for work and compartmentalized the entire event. Five weeks later, as

I was getting ready for work, it hit me. I never even considered the person whose windshield I was going to dive
through. I could have injured or killed her, but that never
crossed my mind.

I ask the peer support class to pretend that today is
the day I just realized what I could have done. I ask them
if I am an awful person for not even considering the
woman who was driving the car and how I could have
maimed or killed her.

Typically, the class is stunned for a moment. I ask
them to remember what I have trained them to do and to
respond with exactly how they are trained—listen, validate, normalize, and educate. Students will start to normalize my fight-or-flight behaviors, educate me about
my normal reactions to this situation, and validate me by
pointing out the bottom line is that I survived. They go
back to their training about the prefrontal cortex shutting
down during the fight-or-flight response and validate the
decisions I made based on the physiology of stress. I ask
them if they can relate this story to another event where
people made a choice to take their own lives and everyone mentions 9/11, when people jumped from the Twin
Towers as the last act of control.

At this point, I congratulate my students for a job
well done. My students realize they can handle any situation thrown at them as long as they go back to the
training.

Students leave day two even more tired but with
some new skills and confidence in their abilities. The

excitement about starting to serve on a team is palpable.

Day Three Morning Content

The first thing we do on the morning of day three is another group quiz on the content of days one and two. Students generally have a lot more questions by day three, as the depths of their responsibilities are clear. We process and problem-solve on every possible scenario either the students or I come up with.

The next concept I teach is what I call the pitfalls. After significant events, trauma has an uncanny way of ruining people's lives. In addition to all the signs of stress and trauma treatment that I have already taught, I address two major pitfalls: survivor high and high-publicity incidents.

Survivor high is the feeling of exhilaration that some people get after they survive a near-death experience or significant trauma. The mindset associated with survivor high is, "If that didn't kill me, what will?" This is a very dangerous attitude, and we saw this in significant numbers as veterans returned from Iraq and Afghanistan. So many veterans without the tools to cope have engaged in very risky behaviors to relive the highs they experienced in combat. Survivor high takes the form of unnecessary risk-taking behaviors. Riding a motorcycle too fast, ignoring safety protocols at work, and pushing the limits in a vehicle around curves are all examples of some of the behaviors we see in first respond-ers who are experiencing survivor high. I train the students on how to ask about the possibility of survivor high, educate the contact if this is an issue, and obtain agreement to alter their risky behavior.

High-publicity incidents are also frequently an issue. While a first responder might find the intense attention from leadership, the media, and the public favorable after extraordinary events, this attention is time-limited and will end. I teach students to remind contacts in this position that the ultimate goal should be to return to normal as quickly as possible. The recognition and celebration after extraordinary events feel great, but this is not permanent. At some point, we all have to get back to normal duties.

I use the example of Robert O'Donnell, the Midland paramedic who was able to free then-eighteen-month-old baby Jessica McClure from the well she fell into in 1987. This was a national event that had significant coverage due to the complexity in getting her out of the well and the duration it took to get the job done. Mr. O'Donnell not only struggled with the event, he also struggled with the decline in attention over time, resulting in his suicide in 1995.

I absolutely encourage my students to learn from these hard lessons and to ask the hard questions to intervene on any fallout that may be harming a first responder's life. They survived the event—the aftermath should not kill them either.

The rest of the morning is spent teaching group interventions. Doing any sort of group intervention properly is vital. I teach two modalities: informal and educational.

An informal group intervention is when first responders are clear to discuss the event and want to compare notes. The ability to hear each other's stories puts the pieces of the puzzle together in terms of the order and the duration of the event. Many times, this is already happening by the time peer support gets involved or it occurs outside of peer support activities. Ask any shift of first responders how they typically out-brief an event, and they will tell you it occurs over breakfast, over beers, or during a backyard BBQ. If necessary, peer support can facilitate these discussions as needed, but I encourage allowing the first responders to take the lead and do this the way they want to. It's their event, and it's theirs to cuss and discuss.

The educational brief is the TEN FOUR Model I developed and shared in my first book. TEN FOUR stands for Triage, Educate, Normalize, Free dialogue, Organize thoughts, Understand the big picture, and Restore resilience. I have already addressed the triage portion of this model in this chapter, and the rest of the model is as follows. From *First Responder Resilience: Caring for Public Servants*, the following is information on the TEN FOUR model.

Educate and Normalize

After triaging a situation, everything should begin with education. First responders in a crisis are rarely inclined to simply open up and start talking. Every agency, organization, department—every customer and every client—gets education first. I do this every time I begin working with a customer, and this means I educate the entire department. To be sure, it is labor intensive and usually involves several briefs, but the payoff is huge.

Educating accomplishes a lot of things: it introduces people to me and me to them. They know who is coming and what to expect. It provides continuing education units. It normalizes and educates first responders. It serves as a pre-incident inoculation and gets them ready for their next incident. It teaches them the terminology I will use after a crisis. It allows them to understand what to expect from me. It assists in their realization that there is a source for help, an outlet to deal with events that might have been ignored previously.

In the aftermath of a crisis, after the stabilization of individuals, I always teach first. Whether I have the luxury of time and am able to do a brief with a PowerPoint or I just have a few minutes in which I need to simply address the next few steps ahead, I always teach first. It assures everyone we are going to take things one step at a time, they are not crazy, and they are going to get through this event.

How much and how long I teach is based on triaging the impacted group. I have several PowerPoint briefs of various lengths to use at any time; what has happened and how people are responding determine the length of the brief I will use. That said, I have walked into situations where I hid my slides because I knew I had too much information for the impacted personnel. And I have walked into situations where the thumb drive in my pocket was never taken out and, instead, I just talked to the first responders.

The most important thing to do is to look at and listen to your people, to know what they are capable of absorbing. The more drastic the incident and the closer the time to the incident, the less they will retain. When you see thousand-yard stares, understand that their attention span is probably about three minutes. Assess your people and trust your gut. This is not your show—it is theirs.

When awful events occur, I simply speak to what is relevant. I address issues to include traumatic grief, the emotional roller coaster after a line-of-duty death, what to expect in the first two weeks, the importance of self-care, healthy

71

stress management, how to talk to family members about what has happened, and the importance of refraining from drinking and driving. I always address this last point, as organizations are more likely to experience this problem in the aftermath of a line-of-duty death.

Each time I brief impacted personnel, as we move further away from the event in duration, I build on what I have already addressed and add new topics, such as preparing for the funeral, how to address the family members of the deceased, ways to organize and help out with the arrangements, the many things that occur after the event, and what to expect during the grieving process.

During the initial briefs, when everyone is in shock and things are very raw, it is possible to pull larger groups together or entire teams together to educate without specifically triaging with the target model. The reason is that you are providing information and answering questions. The task is simply to stabilize and inform. This is the only time, however, that minimal triaging can be done.

Free Dialogue

As things begin to calm down, it is time to move from general educational briefs to emotional processing briefs. These must be handled very carefully. Triaging here is a must. It is imperative to pull the homogenous groups together for these.

To engage the group in the free-dialogue phase, I educate first and simply open it up to discussion by asking the group one or two questions about what has occurred. When groups of first responders are comfortable, they will talk. Sometimes they will sit around and "shoot the breeze" for hours. I usually pass out snacks when this happens. They are on a roll and want to stay and talk. But sometimes first responders simply don't want to talk. There may be dynamics in the group that we are not aware of or pending investigations, when they've been told by attorneys not to say anything. This is their right as well. The bottom line is, they have better education and tools to begin to deal with the event. They also have names and contact numbers to follow up with later.

Organize Thoughts and
Understand the Big Picture

Starting with the bull's-eye in every situation, the peer support team and I will pull those folks together, and after we have covered our role and confidentiality, we educate first. If they have al-

73

ready had some education from us, we build on what we have taught them and educate further. At this point, we open the conversation up to a very informal discussion, in which we essentially ask the first responders to share whatever they are comfortable with. The participants can discuss what occurred, ask questions, or simply vent. It is very informal and easygoing. I do not refer to it as a defusing or a debriefing, I simply refer to it as a brief or briefing. We keep it simple, low-key, and casual. At the end of each brief, we hand out a brochure that normalizes stress reactions and encourages positive coping skills. What happens in these moments of the process is amazing. First responders have the chance to share their perspectives and, for the first time for many of them, they begin to gain insight into what actually happened, they see the entire big picture, and many of the missing puzzle pieces start to come together.

First responders typically walk away from this information sharing with a much clearer picture of the event and a different perspective. The shift in perspective is based on new information and insight, and this usually means they can understand just how severe the situation was. They realize how little control there was and what they were able to do to regain control. This often means closure for most first responders.

From the bull's-eye we move outward, ring by ring, and repeat the process until we are done. As impacted personnel come through the brief, they respond well when it is done correctly. They then tell their colleagues it was helpful, and generally, each brief gets progressively easier due to increased accumulated credibility.

Restore Resilience

As we go through the process, I prefer to keep things real. I hear all the time that first responders who went through a critical incident in the past were told to exercise, avoid alcohol, eat healthy, and avoid caffeine. I don't think this is realistic or appropriate. People are going to do what they do, which might mean eat comfort food or drink a lot of caffeine because they are tired. What I always tell people is, during the aftermath of a terrible incident, it's important to take care of yourself. Go back to the basics of self-care. This means stay hydrated, eat when you can, moderate the alcohol if you are willing, and try to get sleep. If your sleep is disrupted by this trauma, take naps during the day. Try to spend time with your family. Do the things you enjoy. Exercise if you are inclined to do so. Take your vitamins and consider adding extra vitamins C, D, and zinc to get you through this tough time. Ask for help.

Throughout the entire process, we are always assessing how personnel are doing. The peer support team and I make ourselves available for one-on-one time whenever someone wants that. The more time you spend with a group of first responders, the more they will seek out this type of assistance. Peer support members are carefully vetted and trained to listen and guide first responders in problem-solving and healthy coping. They are also aware of what is beyond their capabilities, and they know when it is time to encourage a first responder to see a clinician.

The most challenging aspect of intervening with first responders is the resistance you will meet. Whether this is due to the culture or the fact that they have been through poorly run interventions in the past, you should expect it each and every time you respond to an incident. The key to resolving this is to avoid making it seem like an intervention, but more like extended family showing up to help out any way you can. Pulling this off takes patience, compassion, and strong attention to details. But it works. And it's amazing to watch the transformation of impacted personnel back to healthy and happy.

After teaching the TEN FOUR model, we spend time as

a class practicing the educational portions of this brief so that the team members can get very comfortable with providing the education to both groups and individuals.

Day Three Afternoon Content

As we wrap up the training, I address large-scale events and disasters. We go through the psychological phases of disasters and how to deploy to a disaster. We address the best ways to provide scene support and ongoing care for first responders engaged in disaster management.

In my book, *Code Four: Surviving and Thriving in Public Safety,* I address disaster interventions:

> Caring for first responders during and after large-scale incidents is a vital piece of every deployment. We cannot expect our first responders to deploy or respond to the unimaginable and return to normal operations without a good plan in place to assure this really happens. Being invited to a disaster is an honor and a privilege. It has been some of the most rewarding work in my career.

Control the Chaos

The nature of disasters creates some problems in terms of scene control and the quality of care. In almost every large-scale event I have been asked to deploy to, there are clinicians and peer support or critical incident teams that will just show up to help. This only adds to the chaos and creates confusion, frustration, and causes more problems than help. I strongly discourage self-deployment when I do peer support training, and I prohibit it on teams I manage. I encourage all leaders and incident commanders to promptly remove anyone who shows up uninvited.

After 9/11, I remember seeing therapists who showed up on the outskirts of Ground Zero. Every day, as the first responders were ending their shifts consisting of the gruesome task of digging and finding bodies, these self-deployed therapists would be outside waiting for them. As most Americans were waving flags, cheering the first responders on and thanking them for what they do, the therapists were grabbing their arms and asking them if they needed to be debriefed. You can imagine the responses of the very seasoned, hardened, yet exhausted firefighters and police officers! Personally, it made me sick to see this.

Any team invited to a disaster or large-scale event should remember: this call is a privilege. This is not your glorious victory or some self-aggrandizing moment. This means it is time to go to work, to give it your very best, and stay focused and humble.

Incident command or the leadership in charge of recruiting peer support teams should provide a list and issue very clear instructions to their teams. The list should consist of what to bring, what to wear, what to pack, and what to leave at home. The instructions must be clear and detailed. The moment teams begin to deviate from the list or the instructions will be the moment those teams need to be sent home.

Disaster Mental Health

Prior to deploying, I encourage all departments and agencies to plan and schedule an after-deployment education brief for everyone who goes to the disaster or major event. This should be considered a portion of the deployment and should be a paid event. First responders should commit to the educational brief before deploying.

Once deployed, it is imperative that first responders pace themselves and maintain a consistent and cautious work/sleep schedule. It is very hard to pace yourself when the call to help others and save lives is overwhelming. First responders will work until they drop, which is, of course, dangerous. Not pacing rescuers will cause them to fatigue and be out of commission.

It is far more advantageous to mandate down time.

It is also important to keep fingers on the emotional pulse of how first responders are doing. I strongly encourage appropriate interventions, at the right moment, to enhance first responder resilience.

The first intervention is scene support. I train my peer support teams to do this very important intervention. Armed with water, snacks, sport drinks, gloves, supplies, and anything first responders might need, my teams will "work the crowd" as first responders are taking a break. In doing so, they are not only assisting with the physical needs of the first responders, they are also placing their fingers on their mental pulse to determine how they are doing.

Peer support team members doing scene support will check in with their first responders to see whether or not they have had a chance to call home, how the rest of their team is doing, if they have had enough hydration and nutrition to last them for a while, and to assert what their job assignment is for the remainder of the shift.

As simple as it may sound, it is nonetheless very important work. Peer support team members are assuring that psychological resilience is being maintained and making sure that responders are not overwhelmed.

The second intervention is the educational brief. At the end of the disaster's first day, each person on scene should receive literature reiterating normal reactions to stress and stress management strategies. It is a form of inoculation, because once first responders understand that they are normal and once they know what to do about stress, it will build their resilience. I always refer to the literature as "refrigerator material" and ask first responders to take it home and put it on their refrigerator for their loved ones to read.

Throughout the remainder of the disaster, peer support teams remain available for one-on-one additional advice and education and any form of support needed. They should also be active in post-deployment briefs. The entire process is designed to promote resilience and assure the mental wellness of everyone on scene.

After we address disasters and large-scale incidents, we wrap up the training with any final questions. I tell team members that they are ready, that they will be nervous, and that they should be nervous every time they get called up. It is a very humbling experience to walk into the worst days of people's lives. The responsibility is huge.

Resources and Referrals

The final thing we discuss are local resources, the best referrals to have on hand and how to know when to refer someone to other resources. Peer support students are able to reiterate their role at this point; they know their limitations and they understand that as they provide referrals, contacts are more likely to follow up on those referrals because the recommendation came from a peer support team member.

The best feedback I hear from students is that the events and interventions go exactly the way I taught them. "It was exactly the way you said it would be" is the best feedback I can receive as an instructor.

Final Thoughts

Training is an investment but it is worth it. Insufficient training is a disaster. I worked with a police officer who had been in a shootout with a subject who was pursued after assaulting his mother. The subject wrecked his vehicle, so he got out and proceeded to walk straight toward the officer, firing multiple shots at him. The officer shot the subject eight times, to which the subject had zero pain reaction because of the illegal drugs he had taken.

Peer support from this officer's department showed up at the scene and simply asked the officer if he was ok. The officer replied that he was in fact ok, because that is what all public safety professionals do. The peer support person left the officer at the scene and returned to his off-duty engagements.

After many hours of investigation, the officer was released to drive home. His commute home was over an hour long due to the distance he lives from the city he serves. I asked the officer how much of the drive home he remembered, knowing full well that the answer would be none of it. The officer confirmed this.

This is a horrible, sloppy example of peer support. If a department does not want to invest in proper training and proper protocol, then the department should not bother having a peer support team.

Chapter Five

Respond

Be quick to offer comfort but take time to sit in the mess with them. A willingness to be present can be more impactful than a quick solution.

Brynnen
Austin-Travis County EMS Peer Support Team

For the day-to-day outreaches for personal issues both at home and at work, peer support maintains a steady presence in the lives of the departments they care for. Personal interactions do not require notification to the entire team that a peer is helping someone unless a situation becomes too intense or a contact cannot commit to safety. At this point, the peers know to bring in other team members for assistance.

Large-scale events involving multiple people are obviously a lot more complicated. These require clear communication and ongoing coordination. Step one is to establish the mode of communication. All of my teams utilize an app that allows for group conversation rather than a group text modality due to the fact that group texts can sometimes drop a team member and no one can tell this has occurred.

Once the team is established in the communication app, they are ready to coordinate a response. Typically, the first person to hear about an event puts the information in the communication chain. I then ask every team member to notify the rest of the team whether or not they are available and if they are not, when they will be. Simultaneously, those familiar with the situation begin to update with pertinent information, and the team leaders begin to direct which team members to respond and how to proceed.

The key is to triage and assess the situation to address the needs of the personnel involved. Sometimes the activation is simply dividing up personnel to be contacted later. Other times it is a multi-pronged approach with team members heading to the scene, a hospital, a station, the homes of personnel involved, or wherever they are needed. Team members continue to update their status as they can and request more assistance when they need it. During these events, the communication is very streamlined and extra comments such as "how awful" are not encouraged, as this just adds to the volume of messages that everyone needs to read.

There are also simultaneous phone calls occurring to discuss more in-depth issues that would be too much or too private to put in a communication chain. The best way I can teach is through example.

One event that I assisted with was for a federal law enforcement agent whose adult son committed suicide in their home. A commander called me to notify me of what happened and indicated that peer support was on the way. As we descended upon the situation, there was much to be done. Peer support members divided and conquered. They remained in constant listen-and-support mode for every family member who needed to cry or vent. Food and water were brought to the house, pre-scriptions were picked up, the adolescent daughter was tended to by picking her up from school. Family mem-bers coming from out of town were picked up at the air-port. Meanwhile, the chaplain was on the phone for three hours with a hotel reservations professional as fellow agents from across the country dumped their reward points into an account so that the family and their out-of-town guests and family members did not have to stay in the house. Finally, miraculously, the window that the son broke to get into the house was fixed within a day.

As a clinician, this made my job so much easier. Every need the family had was being met, which al-lowed me to focus on the crisis and trauma work with the family. We worked diligently for several days and then phased the family to other resources, such as a local mental health person, their church, and local grief re-sources.

Another event was an active shooter situation in the baggage claim area of a major international airport. The bull's-eye, first ring, and second ring of exposure to this situation were the main law enforcement entity at the airport.

As a team, the first thing we did was meet with the

port's peer support coordinator to gain her assistance in triaging who was in what part of the target. She was able to compile comprehensive lists and she then set up briefing times for each portion of the target.

For this activation we used the TEN FOUR model. We began with an educational brief for the bull's-eye in this situation. They were skeptical and not happy to be there. We conducted the brief in a boardroom with a large table, comfortable chairs, and plenty of snacks. Within five minutes of starting the brief and discussing fight or flight and acute stress, we had their attention. By the end of the brief they had a lot to say and they stayed and talked informally for two hours. As they left us, the first ring was arriving for their brief. The bull's-eye members stopped to tell the first ring members just how helpful this process was. Each subsequent brief was met with less resistance and even excitement and curiosity about the brief we were giving.

As the days progressed during our time there, a significant number of the law enforcement officers requested one-on-one time with peer support or with me. The word spread about how effective it was to address the trauma in a one-on-one situation. At one point, I had four law enforcement officers lined up in the hallway, waiting for EMDR. The first officer I did it on told the rest that they would be foolish not to take advantage of this opportunity. This is how impactful a successful triage, an effective brief, and a professional team can be in any situation.

Each situation is different. The dynamics of every department are different. The needs of individuals are different. What I ask team members to do is to pause, assess who needs what and when, and then to respond accordingly. Throughout the entire process, flexibility is the key. Circumstances change rapidly and each team's ability to adjust quickly is imperative. Peer support teams often ask for checklists. While you can develop a checklist for a large-scale event, I really prefer that the team gets together, maps out their triage plan, their list of needs, the people they need to access. and to come up with a daily plan. At the end of the day, the team can reassess and plan for the next day.

A local incident involving an auto versus pedestrian is another example of an event with constant triaging and assessing. Unfortunately, the pedestrian was a three-year-old child who saw her sister across a busy street and darted into traffic as she attempted to reach her sister. The driver was not distracted, she simply had no response time. The child's entire family was at a park next to this busy road and witnessed the whole event. An entire kids' soccer game with both teams present witnessed this event. It was awful.

The EMS crews obtained a pronouncement on scene and their agency peer support team met them back at the station to help them clean their ambulances and to give them water and snacks. They had a chance to pull them out of service while the crew took a breather and reset.

Simultaneously, the fire department team did station visits to check in with the firefighters. They were able to assess to assure that they were all ok.

The police officers were on scene the longest due to the investigation. They were far too busy for scene support, and they also wanted to clear the scene as quickly as possible. The peer support team went to the police station to meet them there. In the group activation, I asked the team to stop and get ice cream. Not only did they get ice cream, the peer support team set up an ice cream sundae bar for the officers. As they came off shift, they were hot and upset about the situation. It was amazing to watch their shoulders drop and their spirits lift as they made sundaes and sat down to just decompress and spend time with the team.

Over the next few days, peer support continued to check on the impacted personnel. Meanwhile these personnel (police, fire, and EMS) were able to touch base with each other as they chose to and as they wished. A peer support team member asked me how I knew to bring ice cream. I told them it was more instinct than anything, perhaps a "mom moment." I just figured on a hot, tough day, ice cream would not only help them pause to decompress, it would lift their spirits.

Group Interventions

I want to caution about group interventions. Any intervention that compels people to speak after a trauma is inherently wrong. Every trauma therapist who really knows how to treat trauma will say that we never force or compel our patients to speak about the details of what has occurred. To do so means significantly tearing down a person's defense mechanisms while running the risk of triggering them or causing further trauma.

The other risk involved with a group process where first responders are asked or compelled to speak is that the team has no idea who is being triggered by what is being said, nor can the team control what is being said. In this type of situation, the risk for causing vicarious trauma is way too high. The problem is that first responders typically do not say anything until they leave, which is when they vow to never go through a debriefing again. Meanwhile, the team has no idea they have triggered someone (or several people) and considers the process a success simply because they got the first responder to speak. Verbalizing what happened is not the same as processing in a healing manner. It never will be.

Finally, I want to reiterate the importance of being flexible, thinking on your feet, and assessing each situation. One of my air medical customers responded to an active shooter situation in southern Kentucky. Five helicopters from five different bases in four different states responded to the situation. Within three hours, we had peer support members at each base. Based on the experience and level of exposure, each base had very different experiences and consequently very different needs. Each night during this activation, we met on a conference call and each team member had very different experiences. Some team members had short interventions because the air medical crew had limited exposure, while others ended up staying on the deployment for several days because those crews had seen and dealt with a lot. The key is to never approach any two situations as the same. There are no cookie cutters when it comes to crises.

Chapter Six

Responsibilities

My favorite thing about being on the peer support team is the ability to just be available to help when needed. My listening skills have improved. I have learned that sometimes people don't need all the answers, they may need someone who will just listen to how they feel.

Maureen
Goodyear Fire Department Peer Support Team

When I think of peer support, the word *fellowship* comes to mind. The whole function of peer support is to help colleagues during their most difficult times, both personally and professionally. This is a big role to play in someone's life. When peer support is done well, it mitigates pain and even saves lives. When it is done poorly, the outcomes for first responders have the potential to be worse than receiving no help at all. At all cost, do the right thing. At all cost, do no harm.

Peer support team members need to be genuinely good people who are doing this for the right reasons. Joining a team to use information against others or to exploit them is an absolute disaster. Joining a team as a resume builder is unacceptable and will lead to obvious failures in functioning as a team member. All peer support members should be joining their team because they hate to see their colleagues suffer, and they want to step up and make a difference.

It is important to remember that peer support is not like running a call or dealing with the public, where it is frequently acceptable to give orders and dictate people's behaviors. Rather, peer support is about empowering colleagues to stabilize their situation, put one foot in front of the other, and return to normalcy. This means that team members must be able to pause, listen, assess, understand, offer options, encourage, and follow up. This is quite the opposite from the normal conduct of first responders who are dealing with an emergency.

Everyone has their walls. Our walls are designed to protect us. They keep others out and away from seeing our vulnerabilities. People only let their walls down when they believe they can trust someone.

The role of peer support is never to tear down people's walls. Rather, as I explain in training, the role of a peer support member is to wait patiently on the other side of someone's wall, and to be there when they begin to let the wall down. Maybe they just let the wall down a few inches and peer over, and then they put it up again. Each time peer support is there to listen, validate, and support, it allows the person they are helping understand that they are in control, they can let the wall down at their own discretion, and that the person waiting on the other side of the wall is only there to help.

Recently I did a recurrent training for a law enforcement customer. One of the team members talked about an officer she helped and how, initially, the officer would only talk to her via text. He did not want to talk about the issue he was having, so they simply conversed about the things he did wish to discuss. Over time, they began to text about the issue, and eventually he asked to meet in person. The team member was able to assist the officer until the issue was resolved and stayed in touch with him until he felt everything was completely stable. The fact that the peer support team member took her time, allowed the contact to go at his own pace, and made it clear that he was in control made all the difference. If she had pushed him to speak to her too quickly, it is likely that he would have backed out and maintained that he did not need help after all.

A few months later, the peer support team member's mother died. The officer she had helped reached out to her immediately to see if she needed anything or if he could do anything to help. This is a true testament to the impact she had on his life. People who receive excellent care want to pay it forward.

Boundaries

Another important aspect of peer support is having clear boundaries. Teams find themselves in trouble when they are not adhering to good boundaries. Having clear boundaries is demonstrated in a variety of ways.

The first and most obvious boundary has to do with confidentiality. I strongly discourage team members from speaking about any incident or person they assist for any reason unless it's with another team member who is assisting them. I explain in training that after an event, everyone is curious about how the impacted personnel are doing or about what actually occurred. The colleagues of those who are impacted may seek out peer support members to ask if they are ok or to get details about the event. Even if peer support shares nothing confidential about the impacted personnel, they are always seen as being "in the know" and anything they share can be turned into other words and suddenly the perception is that peer support is violating confidentiality.

I explain to team members during training that if they are at work and other personnel who were not involved in the incident are discussing an event, even if they have all the facts wrong, it is not the role of peer support to correct them. It does not matter how far-fetched the rumor mill has become, the second that team members say, "That's not what happened," the perception is that they are now sharing information. As things get twisted or rumors perpetuated, this creates all kinds of trust issues and possible chaos for the team.

A few years ago, we were doing interviews for team membership with one of my air medical customers. We asked the candidate what he knew about peer support. His answer was by far the best I could ask for, and

I was so excited to hear it. His answer was, "I really don't know much about peer support other than the videos and posters the company has released. We have a team member at our base and once in a while she gets called out, so we cover her shifts. Then at some point she comes back, and we resume normal scheduling. But we never hear about where she goes or what she does." This is such a testament to the team member's commitment to confidentiality and is the exact way to conduct oneself as a peer support member.

Another boundary has to do with interpersonal issues. Team members should never be exploited. They should never be expected to do anything beyond assisting a colleague in stabilizing and finding appropriate resources.

When I began to contract with one of my customers, they had a peer support team that was operating without a clinical consultant. As I stepped into this role, I quickly found that there were some boundary issues that I had to address. One peer support member tearfully told me that she wanted to quit the team because the person she was assisting was demanding money from her. She and her husband had given him money already, and he was demanding more. Somehow in their training, boundaries had not been addressed. When I told the team member that I would address this and that she no longer had to engage in a peer support role with the contact, she was immediately relieved. It turns out the contact had a prescription pain medicine addiction and was using the money to buy drugs. All of this was addressed by the company. None of this had anything to do with peer support.

Another customer that I began to work with also had a peer support team with no clinical guidance. The team had an individual who had just lost his two sons in a car wreck on "suicide watch," where team members would take turns staying at the contact's house. I asked the team leader when this would end and how they could assure the contact would not kill himself after the "suicide watch" ended, to which he had no answers. I was able to intervene, and we were able to get the contact the appropriate level of mental health care he needed. As I sat down with the team, they admitted they were exhausted, stressed, and relieved this was over. While the decision to conduct the team in this manner was made with compassion and concern, in no way was it appropriate for anyone involved.

Another boundary is the interpersonal relationships between peer support, the first responders they are assisting, and the family members. Peer support team members are highly discouraged from forming romantic relationships with those they assist. When a peer support member enters the life of a fellow first responder, the contact is vulnerable. Peer support can quickly become a savior of sorts. The interpersonal chemistry that occurs between those in crisis and the crisis responder is called a trauma bond. While a trauma bond feels very deep, it is based solely on a trauma. Therefore, a trauma bond is actually very superficial. A true bond is a friendship or relationship that stands the test of time with all of the challenges that come along in life. A true bond lasts through illness, childbirth, financial struggles, poopy diapers, in-laws, empty nests, and anything else life throws at us.

While a contact may develop romantic feelings toward a peer support team member who assists them, it is very much up to the peer support member to set those limits by reminding the contact that they are there solely for the purpose of peer support. "We start this process to finish this process" is the mantra I teach peer support teams. This means we are on a mission to get the person stabilized and get ready for the next event, person, or team requiring assistance.

When it comes to assisting the family members of first responders, good boundaries are imperative. In my book *First Responder Families: Caring for the Hidden Heroes,* I address how to manage line-of-duty deaths. This is an excerpt from that chapter:

> During this turbulent time, it is imperative that those in line to assist family members maintain a clear, consistent, steady schedule with clearly defined roles and boundaries. This is how I train my peer support teams for these types of activations, because I have seen things turn drastically wrong.
>
> Specifically, I mandate that my team

members work no more than eight hours a day during activations because the events are mentally and physically draining. I ask them to be ready for me to tell them to stand down, go to the gym, or go home when I notice they are fatiguing or overwhelmed by the intensity of the situation. I do not allow them to work twelve- or sixteen-hour days, because I firmly believe this causes damage to those helping out. The last thing I want is for peer support team members, who are extremely valuable assets, to experience burnout and quit the team.

Additionally, when team members go to the family members' homes, they always go in pairs, and the pairs rotate out every few hours. Many times, I have witnessed one peer support or department team member designated as the family point of contact. They will spend hours with the family, are exposed to significant traumatic grief responses and emotions, get very little sleep, skip their workouts, skip meals, ignore their own families and, at the end of this, are a complete train wreck. They are exhausted, burned out, raw, and out of patience. Their own family is angry and resentful. Put this combination of two very raw people under one roof, and it is the argument of a lifetime. No one is happy, and no one knows what to do about it. This is completely unacceptable.

Another reason those responding need to go in pairs is to prevent trauma bonds. While trauma pulls us together and bonds us in a way that feels very deep and meaningful, a trauma bond is just that—it's a bond based on a trauma. A trauma bond is developed through the feelings of empathy and closeness that result after going through an experience together. It feels exhilarating and sometimes exciting. It is extremely easy to get drawn into a trauma bond. The danger here is that it's a set-up for lines to get crossed and for boundaries to become fuzzy.

Simply put, the danger of one person being assigned to a family is if this person comes from the agency where the first responder worked, they wear the same uniform, do the same job, make the same money, etc. They soon represent the replacement husband, wife, mother, or father. It's a very subconscious pull. It does not start out as intentional. But it happens. It destroys families even more. I have seen it happen, and there is absolutely no reason to create a scenario where this becomes a risk.

Trauma bonds can be a slippery slope for peer support teams, and quite frankly a peer support team member dating or marrying a family member they assisted is the death of the team. One of my customers had an incident they chose to handle without the team. We advised them strongly to let the team come in and, if not, to only allow their personnel to assist the family members in pairs. One of the personnel sent to assist ended up divorcing his wife and marrying the daughter of the impacted person. None of this is appropriate, much less joyful. The supervisor admitted that he should have listened to us. "I told you so" was all I could muster when we had this conversation because believe me, I was super mad to hear all of it.

Following Up

An important aspect of every intervention is the follow up. Peer support members should follow up with the people they help to assure that everything is ok and that the plan (if one was made) is working. Since each intervention and every situation is different, the plan to follow up should be tailored to the situation and the individuals being helped.

The first step is to ask the contact if it is ok to follow up with them. From there, peer support can establish a day and time, as well as the method for contact (phone call, text, etc.). I highly recommend that the peer support member does not schedule this while they are at work. A busy shift means a missed opportunity to call the contact and then the likelihood that the peer support member will forget to follow up completely. It is very important that peer support team members place the follow-up plans in their schedule so they don't forget to make the call. The contact is generally expecting to hear from peer support and when they do not, they can feel abandoned and disappointed.

When peer support follows up, they should be in a place where they can talk. This does not mean locking yourself in the bathroom while your toddler beats on the door. It means being alone, in a quiet spot, and ready to listen. As team members make the call, they should be ready to intervene as well and as thoroughly as they did the first time.

If the contact does not answer, then the team member should leave a voicemail. If texting is an acceptable mode of communication to the contact, the team member should send a quick text as well. At this point, it is up to the contact to return the call or text. I discourage any team member from repeatedly calling or texting the contact.

As the follow up occurs, the team member should assess how the contact is doing, if the plan in place is working, and whether or not more resources are needed. Because peer support is a short-term intervention, if the situation is not improving or if it is worsening, team members must be ready to suggest alternate resources or ideas.

The rule of follow up is three: it is ok to follow up three times. At this point. the situation should either be resolved or other resources are being brought in.

Ongoing Training

Because the skills developed and used in peer support are considered soft skills, they diminish over time. If soft skills are not practiced, team members will lose the ability to listen, begin difficult conversations, and engage in problem solving. Team members become rusty, and when this occurs, they tend to lose confidence.

Ongoing training is a must for all peer support teams. The ability to meet monthly, quarterly, or annually is a great opportunity to practice those skills. In addition, I encourage team members to go through any locally offered crisis intervention, hostage negotiation, or victim advocacy training. Classes hosted by agencies such as the Red Cross are also ways to continue education and skill building.

When the teams I work with come together for training, we typically update first. We cover changes, new policies, latest news, or anything new impacting the team. Then we address a new topic or go more in depth into previously learned topics. It is completely fine to address skills and topics already learned as many times as a team needs to. Most team members benefit from the repetition. Finally, we may do a scenario or a mock activation to work on skills and to pull team members out of the rusty feeling.

I did a training a few years ago for three of my fire departments. The departments are in three cities that all touch each other. If there is a bad incident, the department involved will quickly need the other two departments' help.

We came together as three teams, and the first thing I did was an icebreaker so that everyone could learn everyone else's names. This is a fun game I learned when I was a camp counselor for kids during the summers when I was in college.

We then did some refresher training. I addressed crisis intervention and some of the basic skills I teach in the peer support class.

Simultaneous to all of this, in a separate part of the building, I had actors who were non-peer-support firefighters from all three departments set up and ready for a mock scenario. These actors had arrived earlier than the peer support teams. I explained the scenario and the various roles for each actor. I then instructed the actors to deescalate during the scenario if they felt the team members were helpful, compassionate, and not controlling. On the other hand, I instructed them to escalate if the team members were ignoring them or being too controlling.

The scenario was that a known, local, mentally ill individual had walked into the fire station while the bay doors were up and the entry doors were unlocked and opened fire, killing one firefighter and wounding a second one. In the scenario, the firefighters were told to leave the hospital after their fellow firefighter was pronounced dead and to wait at the administration building. This is where and when the peer support team first entered the scenario and interfaced with them.

The three teams, now operating as one, walked into chaos. Each actor's role encompassed some of the worst things I have dealt with in my twenty-nine-year career. The actors were angry, pacing, disoriented, catatonic, on the phone with their lawyer, and my favorite, the lieutenant who kept saying that they just needed to get back in service.

The team members really had no choice but to jump in, so they did. It was incredible to watch how as they took that first step to intervene (always the scariest part), their own stress decreased, and they slipped right into the role I had trained them for. The team first started with Maslow's Hierarchy of Needs by handing out water bottles, tissues, and baby wipes. They were able to deescalate the actors, allowing them to express themselves without judgment. They listened with compassion and kindness. Before long, the situation was calm.

As we out-briefed the scenario, the team members all maintained that this was initially one of the most uncomfortable and eventually one of the most rewarding trainings they had done. They all agreed that the training kicked in and, as soon as it did, everything began to calm down. To me, this meant mission accomplished.

Referrals

Peer support teams should pull together as many resources as possible and make this information accessible to the entire team. There is much leg work and development effort in doing this, but it is completely worth it to have a great resource guide that is constantly updated. The ability to pass along information, numbers, and other support opportunities is golden. One way to do this is to assign one or two team members to be in charge of the resource manual and to pass this responsibility along to others as needed.

Removal of Team Members

Team members are held to a high standard of conduct and must maintain the integrity of the program. The types of events that would cause a team member to be removed are lack of professionalism with regard to the team, violation of confidentiality, or inappropriate relationships with the first responders they are helping.

If violations occur, team members should be removed immediately. This should be done by the team leader and the clinical consultant, with the administrative person also aware that this is occurring before it happens.

It is a good idea to have team members sign an agreement before the end of initial training. This is an example of a team agreement:

XYZ Agency
Peer Support Team

Letter of Intent

My signature below indicates my commitment to serving as a member of the XYZ Peer Support Team. I understand that serving as a member of this team requires the following commitments and failure to comply with any or all may result in removal from the team.

1. Attendance at the initial training and any other recurrent training as scheduled.
2. Maintain strict confidentiality regarding all interventions and personnel involved.
3. Follow all protocols and directives regarding peer support activity.
4. Organize interventions only with prior knowledge, directives, and consent of the peer support leader or designee.
5. Attend all peer support assignments once committed to do so.
6. Appropriately represent all operations of the peer support program.
7. Never engage in any behavior that potentially reflects negatively on the XYZ Peer Support Team.
8. Maintain open and responsible communication. This includes responding to phone calls and emails in a timely manner.

I also agree that when personal circumstances prohibit my involvement with the team, I will keep the team leaders apprised of my situation and expected timeframe for returning to team activities.

I _____ ,
have read and understand these commitments and obligations and will agree to serve as a volunteer for the XYZ Peer Support Program and abide by all protocols.

_____   _____
Signature   Date

Chapter Seven

Promote

Being proactive and changing the stigma is the key to changing the culture. It is not about hugs and feelings, it is about awareness.

Kyle
Glendale Fire Department Peer Support Team

The first year of operations of a peer support team is vital. Before training ends, there needs to be a clear plan for the promotion of the team. There also needs to be a plan for integration of the program into the culture of the department, region, or county being served.

Promotion involves awareness and consistent reminders. When a team finishes training, I ask chiefs, directors, sheriffs—whoever is in the position of ultimate authority—to announce the team, encourage personnel to utilize the team, and reiterate the importance of receiving help when needed. This is usually done through an email that goes to everyone. Along with the team announcement, I like to attach a picture of the entire team and names as well as contact phone numbers.

Along with the initial email, media is very important. Posters, flyers, or whatever form works for an agency is highly recommended. I ask team members to create posters that grab the viewers' attention and that fit into the culture of the department. Team members who volunteer to create the poster also follow through with getting them framed and hung everywhere we want them to be. The rule of thumb is to hang them wherever first responders go inside any and all of their facilities, but to not hang them where they are visible to the public. I have included some of my favorite posters and logos at the end of this chapter.

For contact information, teams can use an email address or a toll-free number that can be displayed on the poster. I discourage using agency, city, or county email addresses, as those are subject to open record requests and could violate confidentiality. The contact information should be given in the email from leadership and also on every poster or flyer.

I also request that all of my peer support teams be equipped with a dedicated peer support shirt. Whether a t-shirt or a polo, each member needs to be able to put that shirt on when responding to a crisis. The best thing to do is to make the shirt a color that is not used for any other departmental uniform. Team shirts are typically a different shade of blue, gray, or green. I discourage white shirts because they show dirt and these activations can be messy. When peer support members show up in the specific shirt, everyone knows what role they are in. This prohibits peer support members from being pulled into an operational mode, or if they do need to jump into an operational mode, the shirt is a reminder that they need to return to peer support duties as quickly as possible. Shirts can be made with reflective material that say peer support on the back and can have agency logos and patches. The better the shirt, the more visible the team members are.

The other form of identification that I prefer teams have is some sort of daily reminder on the uniform that they are in fact peer support members. This can be an alternate color of an agency identification, a special designation on an ID card that indicates peer support, or even something on the uniform. Some departments identify their members with the words peer support under the rank on uniform shirts. I am not a fan of lapel pins, as these can be easily yanked off a uniform by a combative person or can injure a team member in an altercation. The function of having some sort of peer support designation on a uniform is two-fold: 1) It constantly reminds personnel that peer support is there for them, and 2) It reminds the peer support team members on a daily basis that their conduct reflects on the rest of the team. Even on rough days, team members who are on peer support are reminded by the insignia that they need to maintain professionalism and appropriate behaviors.

The next step is to integrate the team into the culture, hearts, and minds of the department and the people the team serves. As the first few incidents and activations occur, the founding team members will absolutely impact the success of the program. Professionalism, integrity, confidentiality, respect, and compassion will demonstrate to the rest of the department the value that peer support brings to any individual or situation. Consistently good care that is timely is the key. Empowering first responders to overcome adversity and return to normal functioning is vital.

Peer support saves lives. The benefits of a well-run program will pay out far more than the actual costs of running a team. Leaders should consider that their teams are investments and valuable resources. As I train teams, the consensus among team members is a clear identification of how many lives, careers, and relationships that could have been saved had there been a team in place.

About the Author

Tania was three months from completing her master's degree at the University of Texas when she witnessed the dramatic and violent standoff between law enforcement and the Branch Davidian Cult in Waco, Texas. At that point, she knew her calling was to work with first responders and to focus on healing these warriors from the horrors of post-traumatic stress disorder.

Tania spent the first ten years of her career working in a Level II Trauma Emergency Department on weekend nights as she built her private practice during the week. In 2002, Tania transitioned to her private practice on a full-time basis and has dedicated her entire career to working with first responders and military members.

Tania assisted with the aftermath of the Oklahoma City Murrah Federal Building bombing, the 9/11 attacks on the World Trade Center, Hurricane Katrina, the Dallas Police shootings, and numerous other incidents. Tania is referred to as the "warrior healer" by her colleagues, and she is passionate about her work.

Tania resides in Central Texas. Her loves include her family, her pets, and fitness. For more information, please contact Tania at www.taniaglenn.com.

Tania has six other books published by Progressive Rising Phoenix Press:

First Responder Resilience: Caring for Public Servants

Protected But Scared

Code Four: Surviving and Thriving in Public Safety

First Responder Families: Caring for the Hidden Heroes

Smashing The Stigma and Changing the Culture in Emergency Services

This Is Our Normal

CPSIA information can be obtained
at www.ICGtesting.com
Printed in the USA
BVHW030225240321
603329BV00007B/214